CONTENTS

i

INTRODUCTION

Most people, at sometime in their lives, will find it difficult to dress. This may be because they have a temporary disability, such as a broken limb or as a result of a joint replacement, because they are gradually 'slowing down' as they get older, or because they have a more permanent condition, such as arthritis or partial paralysis following a stroke. But, whatever the reason, they need not be subjected to hours of frustration and laborious dressing. Their difficulties can be eased in a variety of ways so that their energy is conserved for more pleasurable activities.

This book provides not only advice on the most useful styles, features, adaptations and gadgets, but also a detailed guide to the most effective techniques for putting on and taking off clothes. Techniques that are appropriately taught and regularly practised will make independent or assisted dressing easier, and/or may enable people to wear more clothes from their existing wardrobes.

The first part of the book will help you to choose the most appropriate garment to wear - taking into account its fabric, style and fastenings - and how to identify the features of individual garments which may help you depending on your particular circumstances or specific disability.

This is followed by a section which contains information about what equipment is available to help you to dress and on how to adapt clothes which you can no longer wear. Details of how you can overcome the difficulties associated with toileting and with various temporary disabilities complete the first section of the book.

The second, and larger half, which is a step-by-step illustrated guide to the various dressing techniques, is divided into two parts: dressing and undressing yourself and dressing and undressing with help. In each part, dressing is described first - although, if you are re-learning skills, remember that undressing is often easier than dressing and should be practised first.

A number of appendices have been included to assist people who want to teach dressing skills and techniques. They provide essential background information on: the development of dressing skills, how to assess dressing capabilities, the best conditions for dressing and the place of dressing in rehabilitation.

ACKNOWLEDGEMENTS

The Disabled Living Foundation would like to thank a number of people who have contributed to the production of this book:

Rosemary Ruston SRN SCM HV, the compiler, who also wrote the book *Dressing for disabled people* on which *All dressed up ...* is based;

Jane Peart, whose clear line drawings enhance the dressing techniques section in particular; and

Diana de Deney and Nicola Stacey, the editors.

Grateful thanks are also due to JD Williams who helped to fund the cost of this book.

1. CHOOSING CLOTHES FOR EASY DRESSING

Everyone enjoys wearing clothes that are comfortable, pleasing to the eye, and that make them feel self-confident. The availability today of such a wide range of styles and fashions should make it possible for everyone - even those who find dressing difficult, either because of a temporary disability (such as a broken arm) or a longer term problem - to buy clothes that not only suit them but also meet their specific needs.

Some people choose specific styles or adaptations that enable them to dress independently, other people are happy to be assisted with dressing so that they can spend more time on other activities of their choice.

Choosing clothes involves establishing a list of personal priorities.

As well as taking into account the ease with which a garment can be put on and taken off, the wearer or the person making the choice may need to ask:

- is it particularly warm?
- does it have seams, folds and pockets which may cause pressure sores on people who have no sensation or sensitive skin?
- will it accommodate and disguise figure shapes or bulky body or limb appliances, eg plaster casts, body braces and calipers?
- is it likely to become entangled in crutches or a wheelchair?
- is it designed to cope with excess saliva?

FABRICS

When choosing clothes, most people are influenced by their style, colour and design. However, the choice of fabric is often equally important. Some people can tolerate clothes made from stiff or itchy fabrics or are happy with garments which crease badly or need a lot of care. For other people, these factors could result in pain or discomfort, or a great deal of wasted time and energy. Correctly chosen fabrics can help to minimise some of these problems.

The following qualities should be considered.

Warmth

Clothes which trap a layer or layers of air next to the body and thus prevent loss of body heat provide the most warmth. A thick fabric with an open structure will trap the most air and is therefore the warmest. In a wind or draught, this should be combined with an outer layer of closely woven clothing which will prevent the loss of this heat from the inner layers. Tight garments, or those which have 'felted' in the wash, restrict air circulation, causing the wearer to feel cold. Warm fibres include wool, silk, acrylic, polyester and fur. Warm fabrics include those with a pile, or those which are quilted or brushed. To ensure warmth, wear:

- clothes with a lining, string vests or loosely knitted garments worn underneath a closely woven one;
- several layers of lightweight clothes, each slightly bigger than the one underneath;
- new garments - which are generally warmer than worn ones.

Warm clothes are particularly important for people with limited mobility who are unable to keep warm by moving about, or for those whose general circulation is poor so that they feel the cold more intensely.

Conversely, some people need to keep themselves cool if, for example, they constantly feel too warm, or are unable to move about in hot weather to cool off. Cool fabrics include cotton and viscose; cool clothes include loose weaves and fine open knits which allow the free passage of air.

Weight

The weight of the fabric may be important because:

- sensitive or painful skin may not tolerate anything heavy next to it;
- heavy clothes may restrict movement and make it difficult for people with weak muscles or painful joints to dress and undress;

Strong fibres, such as silk, cotton or polyester, can be made into fine yarns which, in turn, can be used to produce lightweight fabrics.

Elasticity/stretch

Clothes made from fabrics with some elasticity/stretch make dressing easier. Elasticity also reduces the strain on seams and enables the wearer to enjoy greater freedom of movement. Elasticity is a property of the fibre, while the amount of stretch is affected by the weave of the material.

- Elastic fibres include elastane and Lycra;
- stretch fabrics include knits and those made from crimped or textured yarns;
- stretch clothes include those cut on the bias of the fabric, or those with ribbing.

The degree to which a fabric will stretch depends on the combination of the fibre, yarn and weave. The addition of elastane or Lycra to a fabric will enable it to stretch further - 2-4% is sometimes added to denim, corduroy and worsted weaves to provide sufficient 'give' for a close fit without straining the seams. Clothes of this type are often labelled 'comfort stretch'.

Texture

The fabric texture will influence whether a garment is comfortable to wear. Soft, warm-feeling fabrics, which usually contain a high proportion of natural fibres are the most pleasant.

- Stiff, unyielding materials, eg denim, drill, sailcloth, heavy taffeta or rough tweeds, should be avoided by anyone who has to sit for long periods since they may contribute to pressure sores.
- 'Hairy' fabrics, such as Harris tweed, should be avoided by people with a sensitive skin, allergies or extensive scar tissue.
- Wool worn next to the skin can be irritating and may exacerbate eczema. Although this effect may be reduced if the article is lined, it is probably better to use alternative materials.

Slippery surfaced clothes may cause a person to slide forward in a chair, creating a bad sitting posture, or will hinder carers from obtaining a firm grip during moving and handling actions. Piled, textured or rough weaves, such as corduroy, towelling or velvet, can provide a degree of friction which may encourage a good sitting posture. However, a more supportive chair or cushion would be a better solution.

Absorption/water repellence

Clothes with absorbent properties may be needed:

- if excess sweating causes a person to quickly feel cold or 'clammy';
- because a close fitting body brace, artificial limb or other surgical appliance causes excess moisture, resulting in chafing if it is not absorbed;

- if a person with restricted mobility has to sit for long periods when it is hot;

- because excess saliva or spills of food and drink need to be absorbed quickly by protective garments.

Absorbent fibres include natural fibres and viscose. Absorbent fabrics include knits and towelling

Fibres with poor absorbency include synthetics, acetate and nylon. Fabrics with poor absorbency include close weaves, thin closely spun yarns, thick fabrics, and some with drip-dry and anti-crease finishes.

Some man-made fibres, including nylon, retain odours even when they are washed regularly.

Durability

Clothes are an expensive item in any budget, and those that wear out very quickly can be a major source of expense. Although cheap clothes often appear to be good value, in the long run they may be a more expensive option if they have to be replaced frequently. The exposure of one part of the garment to additional or unusually hard wear may account for the lack of durability. This may be caused by an unusual manner of walking in which the shins or knees may rub together, or by a disabled child crawling or moving about on his/her bottom.

A rough edge or a joint mechanism on plastercasts, calipers, braces or artificial limbs may wear out or cause holes in garments where it rubs. Propelling wheelchairs or using crutches may wear out the inside of sleeves and cuffs or material under the arm.

It may be sensible to consider the following adaptations, especially if the disability is only expected to be temporary:

- the edges of equipment can be padded or smoothed out;

- linings or double panels sewn in when a garment is being made can be very helpful;

- panels of non-woven materials can be sewn or bonded onto the areas of greatest wear, preferably before the garment is worn.

However, in the long term the correct choice of fabric may prolong wear substantially.

The most durable fibres include man-made fibres like polyester. However, fabrics made of 100% man-made fibre can be rather rigid and uncomfortable to wear, so they are usually mixed with some natural fibres to produce a closely woven mixture, eg denim and corduroy made from 75% cotton and 25% polyester.

For discussion about clothes for people who deliberately rip their clothes, see p.26.

Ease of care for your clothes

The type of fabric your clothes are made from will affect the amount of care needed to keep them looking clean and smart. Washing and ironing can be a real chore, especially for people who tire easily and wish to save their energy for more pleasurable activities. No one minds spending a little extra time on a special item, but it is a waste of time and energy to do this for every item. Some types of disability make it impossible for people to care for their own clothes, so that they have to rely on others to do it for them. They may, therefore, try to choose clothes, especially those worn every day, that can be washed easily in a washing machine and need little ironing.

The increasing number of mixtures and synthetic fabrics, fibres and finishes means that it is very important to follow the instructions on the label of the garment, as each type has to be washed and dried in a specific way. The symbols on the labels should correspond with the instructions on detergent and washing powder packets.

Washing

Fabrics can be graded in terms of the temperature and what sort of washing treatment they can withstand. For example, white cotton or linen without special finishes can be washed at a hot temperature, while silk can only withstand a very cool wash.

Some synthetic fibres attract dirt and should be washed frequently as they may be difficult to clean again if they become very soiled.

Because dry-cleaning, although labour saving for the wearer, can be expensive, you may not wish to choose items for day-to-day wear which can be cleaned only in this way.

Tumble drying can damage or shrink fabrics if the correct instructions are not followed. The garments most at risk from this are those which bear the labels 'do not tumble dry' or 'reshape while damp' or 'dry flat'.

Ironing

Ironing is time consuming and can be quite hard work, especially for people with weak or painful hands or wrists, or for those who tire easily. The temperature at which a garment is ironed is important as certain fibres are very sensitive to heat. Some natural fibres, eg cotton and linen, can be ironed at high temperatures, and are easiest to iron when damp. Silk, wool and some man-made fibres, such as polyester and acetate, must be ironed only on a very low setting.

The ironing pile may be substantially reduced by:

- choosing fabrics which have a natural crease shedding ability;
- choosing clothes which can be drip dried;
- using the minimum amount of spin or tumble drying followed by carefully folding the garment as soon as it is dry and cool.

Some 'drip dry' fabrics, such as polyester and polyamides, do not crease easily unless washed at too high a temperature. This causes serious creases which are difficult to remove. Knitted fabrics do not crease easily; viscose fabrics do when wet, but are easy to iron while still damp.

Some garments are labelled 'minimum care' and have a special finish which should reduce the amount of ironing needed. However, this may wear off eventually and the garment may need as much care as any other garment after two or three years.

Flammability

Some fabrics burn more easily than others. However, there is no such thing as a non-flammable fabric, ie one which does not burn at all. The least flammable fabrics are those which smoulder for a long time; brushed or pile fabrics or loose open weaves will burn quite freely. Fabrics can either smoulder like wool, melt like nylon or polyester or flare up like cotton or acrylic.

When choosing clothing, especially for person who smokes, you must take into account his/her ability to recognise danger and put out a fire, should one occur. Clothing is quite difficult to ignite from a cigarette just lying in contact with it, as can happen if a cigarette falls out of the mouth. A hole is the usual result.

The most common fire happens when the lighted cigarette drops onto or down the side of a chair and smoulders for some time in one place before igniting the cover.

For more information, including details on flame retardant finishes and the effects of fabric softeners on the flammability of fabrics, see the DLF's *Fabricwise - fabric choice for people with disabilities.*

STYLES

Clothes that are easy to put on are usually loose, although they must fit properly if they are to look 'right'. It is important that the person is still able to wear styles of his/her choice; therefore, another solution must be found for a man who needs to wear a suit but finds dressing difficult . A different dressing technique (with or without a helper) or 'invisibly' adapting his suit to facilitate independent dressing might be solutions.

The following types of ready-made clothes are easy to put on:

- those that are made in fabrics that 'give' (ie have some elasticity), such as knits or those that use the bias stretch of material;
- those designed to incorporate 'ease' using features such as:
  - fullness - ie gathers which are pleated or pin-tucked into yokes, shoulder seams, necklines etc;
  - deep roomy armholes;
- those with good sized openings and the minimum of fastenings situated in the most accessible places;
- those that are one size larger than usual, depending upon the design of the garment, as long as this is acceptable;
- those that either have no waist seam, or have elasticated or drawstring waistlines;
- 'separates' rather than a dress.

FASTENINGS

As mentioned above, the larger the opening in a garment, the easier it is to put on and take off.

The size and position of the opening is governed by many factors, including:

- if the garment fabric has sufficient 'give' and the style sufficient 'ease', smaller openings without fastenings may be possible, eg T-shirts, track suit trousers;
- front or side openings garments with easy-to-use fastenings are likely to be preferred by most people. However, for people who

need assistance with dressing, back-opening garments may be more convenient to do up;

- openings to below waist level make it easier to step into garments or put them on over the head. Full length diagonal or side front openings are less likely to gape when the wearer sits.

For some people the right number of fastenings in the right place can make the difference between dressing themselves or dressing with help. Think carefully about the type, number and position of openings and fastenings when choosing something new. The ease with which fastenings can be used varies, although it is often fairly easy to substitute one type of fastening for another to promote independent dressing or to speed up the process if assistance is being given. The choice of garments will be wider if you know someone who can make this alteration for you.

The following hints may make dressing easier:

- large, simple fastenings are particularly useful for people with weak, painful or misshapen fingers and hands;

- if bending the elbow is difficult, try to avoid fastenings at the neck;

- if sensation is poor, make sure fastenings can be seen;

- if shoulder movement is difficult or painful, try to avoid back fastenings;

- a fastening that is difficult to do up under tension, may be easier to do up while lying down.

Buttons and toggles

Buttons come in all shapes and sizes and in many different materials. Flattened ball shapes and large, round buttons with a raised edge are the easiest to manage. The weight of the buttons should be matched to the weight of the fabric. Toggles are usually large and cylindrical.

Advantages:

- they will usually remain closed unless the garment is too small;

- they can be a decorative feature;

- they can be fastened with one hand;

- a buttonhook may assist if difficulties are experienced (see p.29);

- the toggle and loop (or frog) fastening is appropriate for heavy fabrics.

Disadvantage:

- small and fancy buttons can be hard to fasten.

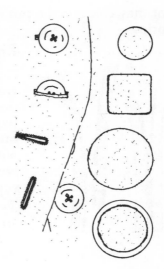

For people with poor co-ordination or grasp, it may be an advantage to either raise the buttons from the fabric by sewing them on with a long shank, backing the top button with a smaller one, or putting two round buttons together.

To avoid fastening cuffs when dressing, sew a cuff button on with elastic and fasten, or make stretch cuff links by linking two buttons with shirring elastic.

Buttonholes and loops

Buttonholes have the following features:

- they can be bound, sewn, be part of a seam or a loop;

- they should be up to 1mm larger than the diameter plus the depth of the button;

- vertical ones are easier to manage than horizontal ones, but come undone more easily when under tension;

- bound and sewn holes are easy to feel.

If you have only one useful hand, it is easier if the buttonhole is on that side.

A garment should have sufficient buttons and buttonholes to ensure that it does not gape.

Loops are easy to manage, as long as there are not too many.

Magnetic buttons

The advantage of having two round magnetic buttons on either side of a front opening garment is that it fastens just by putting the two buttons together. The disadvantage is that the buttons are heavy, so that they can only be put onto outer garments made of heavier fabrics.

Zips

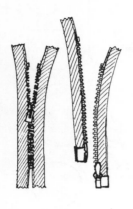

Zips come in a great variety of lengths, weights and colours. They can be open (eg on a jacket), closed (eg on trousers) or two-way. The 'invisible' zip is light in weight but more difficult to open and close. The weight of the zip should be matched to the weight of the fabric.

When in use, the end of the zip being pulled away from must be anchored. When closing an open-ended zip, hold the end with the tag firmly, push the metal tip on the other side into the side of the tag, then pull up. Reverse to open.

Advantages:

- a zip is an easy, smooth fastening which will not gape and will cover the length of the opening;
- an open-ended zip allows a garment to be opened flat.

Disadvantages:

- a zip can catch on flesh or clothing underneath, therefore a firm fabric backing or placket is advisable;
- where there is tension at the top of a zip, eg on a waistband, a further fastening may be required;
- back zips are difficult for those with short arms or painful shoulders - a zipaid may be helpful (see p.30).

If the tag or pull is too small, it can be enlarged by adding a ring, or a leather or fabric loop, so that it is easier to hold (the tag must have a hole in it).

When sitting down in a zipped jacket which extends below the waist, the zip tends to bulge or the jacket to curl up. A two-way zip, or opening the side seams to the waist, may help.

Zips can replace laces on shoes; a dressing stick (see p.27) can be used to pull up the tag.

Buckles

Buckles are normally found on belts or shoes and are frames of metal or similar material, with one or more prongs usually attached to a central upright. There are usually a number of holes at intervals along the belt. Buckles with several prongs on webbing are usually found on surgical corsetry.

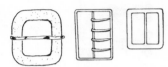

Advantages:

- buckles provide a firm fastening and can be decorative;
- buckles are difficult to undo accidentally;
- a fixed buckle, eg on a shoe, can be done up with one hand.

Disadvantage:

- small buckles can be difficult to handle.

A buckle with several prongs threaded onto webbing is useful, as there is no need to match the prongs with a hole; however, the prongs must lie flat or they will catch on other clothes. Buckles without prongs need a firm fabric belt so that it does not move; alternatively, a Velcro dab, press stud or hook and eye must be added at the end to fix it.

Hooks and eyes, hooks and bars

These fastenings are available in many sizes; the larger ones are probably the most useful although they can be bulky; the smaller ones are flatter and neater.

Hooks and rings are more difficult to fasten than hooks and bars. They are widely available as a sewing accessory and therefore can be used as a substitute for other fastenings. Hooks and eyes/bars are now mostly used for corsetry and trouser waistbands

Advantages:

- they are flat, invisible fastenings;
- the hook and bar is easy to handle on waistbands, and can be fastened under tension.

Disadvantages:

- small hooks and eyes are hard to see and feel.

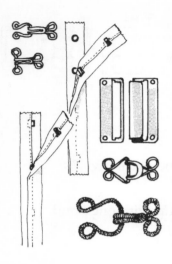

Prising the hook apart a little may make it easier to fasten. People with the use of only one hand may find the Kempner fastener (see below) or a D-ring/cynch fastening (see below) easier to use on corsetry. Small hooks and eyes can be replaced with larger ones.

If it is difficult to anchor the bar on a waistband, sew a loop on the end of the waistband, pull the loop well beyond the bar; let the loop move back close to the waistband and the hook should catch on the bar. Lie down to reduce tension. (This only works on a non-elasticated waist-band.) The hook is put in more easily by folding back the fabric behind the eye.

Kempner fastener

This is a hook and bar with a strap and is very suitable for one handed users.

The bar must be stabilised and there must be enough grip to place the hook over the bar and to pull the bar to tighten or loosen it.

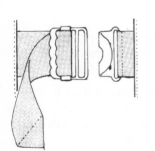

Advantage:

- it can be used with one hand.

Disadvantage:

- it is bulky, perhaps best used on corsetry.

If a person only has the use of one hand, the pull should be towards the functional hand. The free end of the strap can be stitched back to prevent it from being pulled out of the bar; this can be made into a loop if the wearer finds the strap difficult to grasp.

Cynch or D-ring fastening

This is a strap and a D-ring. The strap is sewn on one side of the opening and the D-ring on the other. A Velcro dab is sewn on each end of the strap. The strap is passed through the D-ring, and then doubled back to the original side where it is fastened using the Velcro. This type of fastening is often found commercially on shoes, but can be used as a substitute for a fastening or as an anchor so that other fastenings can be done up under less tension.

Advantage:

- it can be fastened firmly with one hand.

Disadvantage:

- it tends to be bulky.

If used with one hand, ideally the strap should start and finish on the able side.

Tapes and laces

Tapes are normally made of fabric, laces of cord. Laces are usually found on shoes, cagoules and anoraks, tapes on aprons and neck fastenings.

Advantage:

- they make a garment fit quickly and adjust easily.

Disadvantages:

- tapes behind the back are difficult to fasten, the knots can be painful to lie on or cause pressure sores;

- the ends can catch in wheels, doors etc;

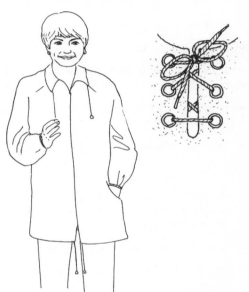

- tapes can be torn off especially when being washed, and knots which have been washed and ironed are difficult to untie;

- it is difficult to tie a knot with one hand.

Laces can be replaced by elastic, particularly in shoes.

Velcro

Velcro is a type of fastening available on very few ready-made

products. However, it lends itself to being a replacement fastener for many types of opening.

There are two sides to a Velcro fastener; one with many tiny hooks, the other with many loops, When they are brought together, the hooks catch onto the looped material forming quite a strong bond. The hook side should always face away from the body. For general use, it is best used in short 2-cm 'dabs', rather than in strips as it is easier to line up, is less damaging on fine fabrics and is obviously cheaper. However, if using it in situations where the fastening is under tension, eg on a waistband, a strip of at least 5cm will provide a stronger hold.

Advantages:

- it is easy to use;
- it can replace many conventional fastenings, eg buttons, zips and buckles;
- it is more comfortable to lie on than buttons or zips at the back of a garment;
- it is available in a variety of colours and widths.

Disadvantages:

- it must be closed before laundering - lint from other garments can catch in the hook side, making it unusable (it can be cleaned with a special brush) and can damage other clothes;
- it makes a tearing sound when being unfastened;
- the hook side can snag on other clothing, especially stockings or woolly materials;
- it can come undone if the length of Velcro is too short;
- it is not always easy to line up properly.

Where it is used instead of buttons, sew the buttons over the buttonholes for appearance.

Press studs, poppas

Press studs come in many sizes and can be sewn on or riveted. Poppas can be hammered on or attached with a special tool. They are often used on jackets.

Advantages:

- they make a neat, flat, invisible fastening;

- the smaller sizes are easier to pull apart;

- they can be closed with one hand when there is a firm base to push against.

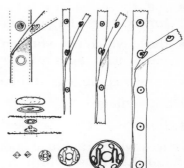

Disadvantages:

- old or worn ones can undo when under tension.

A button sewn over the top of a press stud makes it easier for someone with poor grasp or co-ordination to hold onto. Large press studs and poppas should be fixed onto strong, firmly woven fabric or be well backed.

The following have unique types of fastening which warrant a special mention.

Braces

Some braces have clips and some have buttons.

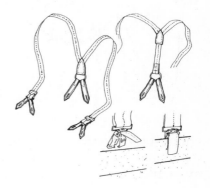

The easiest way to fasten braces is to attach them to the trouser/skirt waistband, pulling the garment up and bringing the loops over the shoulders. Alternatively, it can be done by putting the garment on, attaching the braces to back of waistband, bringing the straps over the shoulders, and fastening them at the front.

Advantages:

- when held over the arms during toileting, they prevent the trousers from falling down;

- they can be used as a dressing aid to pull garments up from the floor;

- the trouser/skirt waistband can be a larger size which will, in turn, create a larger opening;
- those which have buttonholes can keep pants up as well (the pants need tapes in the right places to thread the braces through);
- some people regard them as a fashion accessory.

Disadvantage:

- those with clips can be difficult to do up.

Braces which divide at shoulder blade level stay on the shoulders better than those which divide lower down. Braces with buttonholes need buttons on the garment in the right places.

Edgware braces

The Edgware Braces are especially useful during toileting for people who only have the use of one hand as there is no need to remove clothes worn on top or to unfasten the braces. Pants should be attached to the trousers with Velcro so that they can be let down together.

To lower the trousers, undo the waist fastening and then undo the Velcro beneath the button. To bring the trousers up, the Velcro is refastened. The unfastened braces should be long enough for the trousers to hang at the base of the buttocks so that the trousers can be pulled aside easily. A pattern for the braces is available from the DLF (send sae please).

Suspenders

Suspenders are adjustable straps, usually made of elastic, which are found on corsets and suspender belts. They have a device which is usually used to hold stocking tops, although they are used occasionally for socks. A similar sort of clip is used on dungarees to hold up the bib front.

They are fastened by holding the bobble firmly underneath the stocking welt or dungaree bib, placing the loop over it and pulling tight.

Advantages:

- they keep stockings up and a corset pulled down. Front can be fastened when seated.

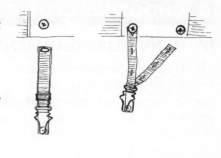

Disadvantages:

- they can be difficult to fasten under tension and at the back, or if the wearer has poor co-ordination, sensation or grip;

- the back suspender can cause pressure when sat upon and should therefore be moved to the side if the wearer is seated all day.

One way of managing suspenders more easily is by separating them from the garment, attaching them to the stocking and then re-fastening. For example, sew a loop or a large hook to the suspender and a button or an eye on the garment, or sew both suspenders together at an angle so that only one loop or hook is needed. There are normally two for each stocking, front and back. The back suspender can be moved to the side without loss of effectiveness.

Alternatives to suspenders and stockings include tights, grip top stockings, socks or popsocks, or no stockings at all.

2. CHOOSING CLOTHES FOR SPECIFIC FEATURES

BY INDIVIDUAL GARMENT

The different features of various types of garments which may be helpful to someone depending on his/her particular circumstances are discussed in this section. Most are available from normal retail sources, although some are especially designed with the dressing difficulties of elderly or disabled people in mind.

Garments which have features common to both men and women are described first. Other garments and features are mentioned in the appropriate section. A number of the features have already been described (see p.7).

Unisex clothing

Outerwear

Tops

Where appropriate, shirts, blouses T-shirts etc are best worn outside skirts/trousers. The front of straight styles lies more smoothly if the side seams are open from waistline to hem. If worn inside, there should be adequate tuck-in.

The traditional man's shirt is difficult to put on and fasten. Look for casual styles made from a knitted fabric which stretches more easily, but can also be worn with a tie. Some shirts have a pleat in the shoulder or back yoke seam which gives added fullness (many uniform shirts are designed like this.).

Drop shoulder seams are usually found in casual shirts, raglan sleeves are rare. T-shirts are comfortable and can be found in many styles; they are always made from knitted fabric.

Trousers

Stretch or elasticated waistbands are comfortable and make dressing easier. Fabrics containing Lycra will have extra 'stretch' to make dressing even easier, and the knees of garments will not get 'baggy' so quickly. Waist adjusters are available on some styles.

Tight fitting trousers may be very uncomfortable if you have to sit all day; they are also difficult to fasten at the waist. Those with pleats in the front are more comfortable and can disguise a sagging stomach. Using braces makes it possible for trousers with larger waistbands to be bought (see p.15).

Tabards, ponchos, sleeveless pullovers, body warmers and waistcoats

These are easy to put on, add warmth without adding too much weight and disguise awkward figure shapes.

Leisure wear

Jogging outfits and leisure suits are easy to wear, attractive, warm and are suitable for many occasions. Many have elasticated waists and those without fastenings are stretchy and very easy to put on and take off. Some have zips at the ankle, which may help to accommodate calipers, plastercasts etc.

Outdoor wear

People who are susceptible to the cold need to conserve body heat. Coats and jackets should be lightweight, perhaps padded, and as windproof as possible to avoid wind-chill (excessive cooling of the body by the wind). Satin-type linings enable garments to be slipped on easily.

Accessories

Hats are essential in winter as a substantial amount of heat can be lost through an uncovered head. Scarves and gloves should also be worn.

Scarves, high collars and loose, large polo-necks can disguise a surgical collar.

Nightwear

The British Standard on Flammability and Night Attire (BS5722) applies only to children's garments. Because fabrics used for adults' nightwear do not have to be tested or conform, serious burns have resulted from fires in the home. Sensible choice of style can minimise this danger.

Nightgowns, nightshirts and dressing gowns

Short length garments are safer than full length, particularly when going up and down stairs. Many nightshirts are open fronted.

A button-through nightshirt is easy to put on and avoids the need for pyjama trousers.

Long sleeves should be close fitting to avoid catching fire from an open fire or gas cooker.

Split-back garments can be put on and taken off without the wearer having to stand; back flaps can be tucked into a belt at the front when using the toilet. This style is unpopular with some people because it accentuates their disability. Overlaps should be generous, at least 20cms. These are normally available from specialist suppliers.

Pyjamas

If you find it difficult to move about in bed, styles made from smooth shiny fabrics, such as satin, polyester or nylon, can help.

Brushed fabric pyjamas with cuffs at wrists and ankles are warm.

Pyjama trousers and tops can be bought separately.

Women's clothing

Underwear

Bras, vests and petticoats with broad shoulder straps will 'stay put' more easily.

Underwear made of man-made fibres may produce a lot of static electricity; cotton underwear does not and is cooler in hot weather.

Bras

Many different bras are available including sports and sleep bras. Front opening bras are easy to fasten when lying down. If a fitted style is uncomfortable, a liberty bodice or crop top can be worn instead. It is a good idea to be measured if your figure changes.

Back fastening bras can be fastened at the front and moved round to the back.

A bra slip reduces the number of garments to be put on.

Vests

Vests conserve body heat. For anyone who is inactive, long sleeves and long body styles are warmest.

Short camisoles or spencers (short vests) may be best for those who sit for long periods or have a continence problem.

Seamless vests are more comfortable under a body brace - most adult T-shirts have no side seams. Vests with buttons at the neck or combinations have larger neck openings.

Petticoats

Garments put on over a smooth nylon or satin petticoat should slide down over it easily, but may produce static so that the top garments cling to it. The smooth surface could also cause the wearer to slide forward in a chair.

It may be easier to 'step into' a waist slip.

Pants

Pants are available in a great variety of styles. High legs have no elastic. Long leg pants are warmer. Mini briefs are easy to push down.

Cami-knickers (teddies) combine vest and pants, while 'bodies' combine tops and pants. These garments are put on over the head, and the crotch fastening avoids the need to pull pants up and down. The flap has to be moved out of the way while on the toilet.

Crotchless knickers also make it unnecessary for the wearer to pull pants up and down, but two hands are needed to draw the two sides apart. The gusset on very wide legged french knickers can be pulled to one side when going to the toilet.

See DLF leaflets CC1 - CC4 .

Foundation garments

Open flat corsets may be easier to put on lying down.

Zip fasteners are easier to do up than hooks and eyes. (Enlarge the zip pull if necessary.) Some people find laces at the front helpful, especially if the waistband has to be adjusted.

Suspender belts or liberty bodices are alternatives to corsets. A liberty bodice is a combined vest and suspender belt which buttons down the front.

Suspenders at the back can be extremely uncomfortable to sit on, so move them to the side.

A short corset is best when sitting for long periods.

Hosiery

Hosiery is available in natural fibres, man-made fibres and mixes and also in varying lengths. Care needs to be taken that 'stay-up' stockings and pop socks are not too tight, particularly if the wearer has poor circulation.

Hosiery in dark colours which blend with an outfit makes legs less conspicuous. Patterned, textured hose and light colours can make thin legs look plumper.

Cotton tights with a gusset can be converted to an open style by removing the gusset.

Skirts

A-line styles, which are smooth over the hips, drape comfortably over the knees when the wearer is sitting and are easy to lift out of the way when using the toilet.

Adjustable wrap-round styles and skirts with fully elasticated waistbands are easy to put on. Permanently pleated styles need minimal ironing and drape well; pleats from the hips look attractive over the knees.

Tight skirts crease over the stomach when someone has to sit for long periods.

Men's Clothing

Underwear

Long-sleeved and long-bodied vests provide the most warmth.

Pants

Both boxer shorts and slip briefs are easier and quicker to manage than Y-fronts.

For adaptations and further information, see DLF leaflets CC2 and CC3.

Ties

Clip-on or ready-tied ties save dressing time.

The books *Clothes sense for disabled people of all ages* and *Fashion for disabled people* look at ways in which clothes can enhance the way you look and show you how to make the best of whatever styles are available at the time.

FOR PEOPLE WITH SPECIFIC DISABILITIES

This section lists a number of general problems and suggests the types of clothes that may help to overcome them.

For someone who has difficulties with shoulders or arms

- Avoid clothes with traditional, set-in sleeves and fitted backs - styles with large, deep armholes and/or a 'full' (ie gathered) back are much easier to put on.

- Clothes with the following features are easier to put on:
  - garments with dropped shoulders, batwing, magyar, dolman or raglan sleeves;
  - stretchy fabrics that 'give', eg knits and all styles cut on the bias;
  - a dress opening which extends below the waist can be stepped into /out of rather than pulled over the head;
  - wrap-over or open-front skirts and styles with large or stretchy neck openings.

- If you are unable to avoid back-fastening styles, fasten the garment at the front and then move it round to the back.

- Minimise shoulder movement by resting the elbows on a table.

For someone who has difficulties with fingers

- Choose clothes which have few or no fastenings.

- Zips and buttons must be easy to see and handle.

- A zip can be made easier to pull if a tag or finger-sized ring is attached to it.

- Trousers and skirts with elasticated waistbands need no fastening.

- Magnetic fasteners may be easier to handle.

- Velcro is a useful fastener for shoes and can be substituted for fastenings on clothes.

- Larger buttons and press studs are easier to handle than small ones.

- Try slightly larger, lightweight clothes of stretchy fabrics and Velcro-fastening corsetry.

- Open crotch knickers may be more convenient.

For wheelchair users and those people who have to sit for long periods

Because most clothes are designed to look their best when the wearer is standing up, they may not 'hang' or fit correctly on a person who spends most of his/her time in a seated position.

'Wheelchair' trousers with a longer back seam, shorter front seam and longer leg length are now widely available from specialist clothing companies. Someone who has to remain seated for most of the day, will find that, gradually, his/her waist will tend to thicken and that the hips will broaden, while using a manual wheelchair often causes the shoulder and upper arm muscles to increase in size.

These factors need to be taken into account when choosing clothes:

- elasticated or half-elasticated waistbands give additional fullness;
- pleated or gathered styles will disguise waist or hip thickening;
- A-line or gored skirts are more comfortable, and longer skirts which fall over the knees are usually more attractive;
- a wrap-over style of skirt or one that fastens completely down the side is easy to put on, and can also be left on the chair seat during toileting. A side-fastened skirt will not pull across the front;
- elasticated waists on dresses can often feel as if they are in the wrong place. Co-ordinated separates can make an outfit look like a dress. Different sizes of tops and skirts are usually available;
- sleeve styles of the type mentioned on p.23 allow for enlarged shoulders;
- cuffs and long sleeves should be close fitting at the wrist so that they do not catch in the wheels of the chair or become a hazard in the kitchen;
- jackets and coats should be short at the back so that they are not sat upon;
- slits in the side seams at waist level avoid strain over the hips. Double ended zips can be opened to the waist to prevent the zip from curling up;
- tight fitting trousers may be uncomfortable unless Lycra or similar elastic fibre is part of the fabric. Thick seams, particularly at the back, are best avoided. Particular care should be taken with jeans or with garments made from similar hard fabrics;

- patch or diagonal pockets at the front of skirts or trousers are easiest to put items in. Back pockets are uncomfortable to sit on, difficult to get at, and can cause problems if skin sensation is poor.

For more hints, see DLF leaflets CW1 and CW2.

For someone with height loss and/or curvature of the back

- Colour-co-ordinated outfits, hosiery and shoes create an appearance of height.

- Co-ordinated separates look like a dress but the waistline can be adjusted so that the hemline remains constant.

- To disguise and hide round shoulders or a curvature of the spine caused by osteoporosis, choose a bodice style which is gathered, tucked, pleated or smocked into the shoulder yoke or seams.

- Tops with large flat, frilled or sailor-type collars can help, as can a shawl flung casually round the shoulders, or wide lapels. Shoulder pads help to build up sloping shoulder(s).

- Men usually wear separates but find jackets a problem because they are normally straight-backed.

- Cape-style raincoats can help to disguise curvature of the spine; belts make it worse.

Adaptations of paper patterns are available from the DLF. For further clothing information, contact the National Osteoporosis Society(PO Box 10, Radstock, Bath BA3 3YB) or the Scoliosis Association UK (2 Ivebury Court, 323-327 Latimer Road, London W10 6RA).

For someone with a disease of the nervous system

People with a disease of the nervous system are likely to suffer from fatigue, cold, muscle wasting, excess saliva and continence problems.

- To counteract fatigue, clothing should be lightweight with easy fastenings or garments which are two in one. Loops on pants and underwear may be helpful.

- To counteract cold, thermal underwear from ski ranges, heat pads, and electrically heated clothing may help (see DLF leaflet *Dressing for warmth*). Pre-warming clothing before putting on may help.

- To counteract muscle wasting, use dressing time to exercise muscles.

- The DLF leaflets *Clothing for people with excess saliva* (C3) and *Clothing for continence* (CC1-4) will provide addition information on these subjects.

For people who deliberately rip, or take off, their clothes

Since the destruction of clothing, which is a distressing symptom of disturbed behaviour, may become a habit, prevention is the best form of management.

Garments made in strong or stretchy fabrics or clothes which are difficult to take off will not necessarily eliminate the problem since such behaviour is often one of the ways in which the wearer tries to communicate. If the wearer is unable to make him/herself understood in this way, then another equally anti-social way may be sought.

The only long-term solution may be psychological help but, in the short term, garments made in the fabrics described above or clothes which are difficult to take off may provide short term relief.

Distracting or occupying the wearer in some way, or making sure that he/she likes the clothes being worn may also help.

- A close plain weave of 100% man-made fibres is probably the strongest fabric but is most unpleasant to wear, and could even make the wearer more destructive.
- Fabrics containing elastane (Lycra) may be suitable because, when strained, the yarns will stretch to some extent instead of breaking.

The style of garment is as important as the fabric:

- short sleeves are less accessible than long; sleeves which end in a cuff will be more vulnerable than ones which do not;
- a full-length garment, like a jumpsuit, may be less easy to take off;
- round necklines may be harder to tear;
- decoration added to clothes may be torn off; it should always be incorporated into the garment;
- raglan sleeves or drop-shoulders may be less vulnerable than set-in sleeves;
- seams should be double sewn, and all sewing well finished, particularly in the areas which are likely to be picked at. Binding openings may help.

3. MAKING USE OF YOUR ORIGINAL CLOTHES

DRESSING EQUIPMENT

Various items of equipment are currently available on the market which can be used to assist with dressing. They tend to be used:

- as a long term solution to a dressing difficulty; or
- as a help towards independence, when they should be discarded as soon as possible.

It is advisable to seek advice from an occupational therapist before purchasing any equipment. Remember that a gadget may not immediately make dressing a quick and easy activity; a lot of practice is usually needed. However, practice makes perfect!

Dressing stick

A dressing stick is a length of wooden dowelling which is rounded at one end and often has a rubber thimble or a hook at the other. A hand grip increases the diameter of the stick. It may be helpful for people with poor grasp or with arthritis. The stick should be tailored to suit the needs of the person using it, eg the dowelling can be cut to size.

Function:

- to bring clothes round, or push garments off shoulders;
- to pull up zips (with the hook);
- to tighten or loosen laces;
- push clothes down, eg pants, stockings;
- to pull up straps;
- to put stockings/socks over the feet and drag them up the legs (with the thimble).

How to use:

1. hold the stick where it feels most comfortable;

2. carry out activity required.

Alternative:

• a wooden coathanger with the centre hook removed.

Reachers or pick-up sticks

These are commercially made with a pistol-type handle and pincer grip.

Function:

• to pick up clothes from the floor.

How to use:

1. grasp the handle and lower the pincer end onto garment;

2. squeeze the 'trigger' and pick up.

Alternatives:

• avoid dropping clothes on the floor, perhaps by hanging them over a chair;

• attach braces, loops or tapes to clothes which can be held onto or looped round furniture;

• use the crook end of a walking stick to pick up clothes.

Sock and stocking aids

Sock and stocking aids are commercially made items which can either be flexible or firm. The flexible gadget, made of plastic, is cone shaped with a rounded end. It has two holes for tapes at the top and two good sized notches below them. A double one can be used for tights. The firm gadget consists either of a circle of plastic with tapes or a handle, or is a floor-standing model.

Function:

• to put on hosiery.

How to use (full instructions are normally given with the item):

1. feed the hosiery onto the gadget (ensuring that some of it is firmly tucked into the notch of the flexible model);

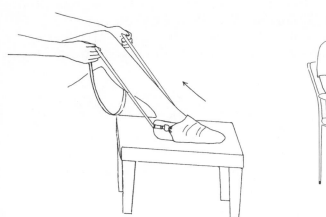 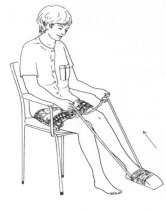

2. put the foot in and pull up the leg with the tapes/handle. A little talcum powder helps the foot to slide more easily.

Alternative:

- use a crook handled walking stick to manoeuvre the hoisery.

Light and medium support stockings can usually be put onto one of the firm or floor-standing gadgets, although the user needs to have flexible ankles to use these.

Gadgets are now coming on to the market to assist with the application of compression stockings. However, they are designed to be used by people who have a full range of hand and leg movements and may therefore be difficult to use if you have general dressing difficulties.

Buttonhook

A buttonhook is a commercially made gadget with a thick handle and a hook or two crossed wires.

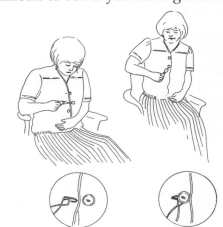

Function:

- to assist with fastening buttons.

How to use:

1. hold the handle and place hook or wires through buttonhole and put round shank of button;

2. bring through buttonhole by turning the wrist to bring the elbow outwards and upwards. This needs quite a lot of practice, particularly when doing it with one hand. It helps if the edges of the garment can be held steady, and if the buttonhole is on the able side.

Zipaid

A zipaid is a piece of cord or fine chain with a hook at one end and a tab at the other.

Function:

- to open or close a back fastening zip unaided.

How to use:

1. insert the hook of the gadget into the zip tag before putting the garment on;

2. put the garment on, pull on the base of the garment to stabilise the zip;

3. find the end of the zipaid and pull up;

4. tuck the end down the front of the garment;

5. in reverse, flip the zipaid down the back and pull the end while grasping the neckband/collar to stabilise the zip.

Alternative:

- avoid back-fastening garments!

Loops

Loops can be made of tape or ribbon, and sewn on wherever they are needed.

Function:

- to bring garments nearer to the body, making it easier to do up a fastening;

- to hold onto or to drop a garment down.

How to use:

1. slip thumb, hand or fingers into the loop or place it over the thumb or fingers of the other hand.

Loop ladder

This is a 'ladder' made of loops fastened together, with a clip or peg at one end. Two are needed if you are putting on trousers or a skirt.

Function:

- to pull up trousers or a skirt.

How to use:

1. attach clips to waistband;

2. throw garment to the foot of the bed, while remembering to hold onto the last loop;

3. put feet into garment and pull on ladder 'steps', reaching for the next one as each one is reached;

4. remove clip once waistband is in place.

Trouser aid

This is a plastic loop which attaches to waistband of trousers by a button and loop fastening, and has a strap attached to its top edge. Trousers can be pulled up using the strap, without bending.

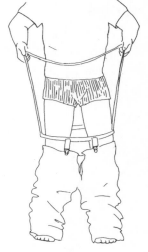

Elastic laces

Function:

- to put on shoes without bending down.

How to use:

1. thread shoe as usual, ending with a bow;

2. put shoe on with a shoehorn. If the tongue gets in the way, attach it down one side, or make a hole in the tongue and thread the lace through it.

Shoehorn

Function:

- to assist people who cannot bend to put on their shoes;

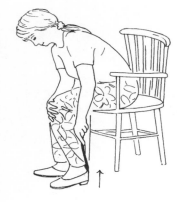

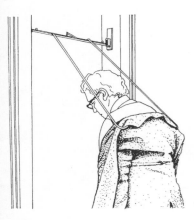

- they are necessary to help people who have shoes with elastic laces or elastic-sided shoes.

How to use:

1. place toe into shoe and slip shoehorn behind the heel;

2. ease the heel down the shoehorn into the back of the shoe.

Dressing rails

These commercially available rails are fixed to the wall.

Function:

- to give support when standing up to dress.

How to use:

1. place clothes in order on rails;

2. hold on to rail with one hand while using the other to pull up or pull off garments.

Coat-on

This device was designed solely for putting on coats and jackets. It comprises two brackets fixed inside the doorframe on which the coat is held. The person puts his/her arms into sleeves, steps backwards to pull coat over arms and shoulders, then forwards to release coat.

Boot remover

This is a rectangle of wood or firm plastic with a V-shaped hole in one end, and raised on a peg behind and underneath the hole. It is very useful for removing wellingtons and other high-legged boots.

Function:

- to provide a firm base against which footwear can be removed.

How to use:

1. undo the shoe and ease fastening;
2. put the heel into the V-shaped hole, using the other foot to stabilise the boot remover;
3. bring heel upwards to take foot out of the shoe.

Alternative:

- use the other foot.

Mirror

Function:

- to remind the dresser what the garment looks like, the position of fastenings and how far he/she has progressed with dressing;

- to remind the person what the body looks like, particularly if the user has had a stroke.

- it can also be used as a teaching tool. Dressing is usually taught by the teacher standing in front of the learner, so that dressing is learnt via a mirror image (left and right reversed). A mirror enables the teacher to stand behind the learner so that he/she can see what is being done and reproduce it more easily.

If a mirror increases confusion it should not be used.

Marking clothes

Function:

- to distinguish between right and left, inside and outside of a garment (see p.106).

- to assist people with a visual impairment.

Conceptual difficulties

To make it easier to identify right and left, clothes can be marked with different colours or with embroidered symbols, such as a cross or a circle. Left and right can be taught using shoes and gloves. Most clothes have a manufacturer's tab inside at the back, which can help the dresser to distinguish back from front, inside from outside.

Visual difficulties

Visually impaired people usually develop a greater sensitivity to touch which will enable them to feel the differences between fabrics, shapes and designs, the positions of seams and the manufacturer's tab. Shape buttons, available from the Royal National Institute for the Blind (RNIB), can help them to identify matching garments accessories and colours.

ADAPTATIONS

Few people can afford to change the clothes which are no longer wearable, especially if the disability is a temporary one or if it is the result of an accident or acute illness. Adapting existing clothes may therefore be the only solution.

Adaptations may also be necessary if your needs cannot be met easily by existing clothes on the market, and if you cannot find the required styles and colours

Most of the adaptations described here enable the wearer to put garments on and take them off more easily, ie they change the position or length of garment openings and the type of fastenings used. Opening seams and adding loops of tapes or elastic are also described.

If possible, adaptations should be undetectable when the garment is worn, or should be incorporated as a decoration.

Openings

Velcro and zips are the most unobtrusive fastenings when opening the seams of sleeves or trouser legs.

When lengthening an existing opening, either unpick an existing seam or, if the fabric has to be cut into, make a placket and add fastenings. When extending the fly seam of trousers, extend the placket as well.

Replacing fastenings

Preserve the normal appearance of the garment wherever possible, eg if Velcro is substituted for a button and buttonhole fastening, stitch the original button on top of the buttonhole.

Velcro can be used when an adjustable fastening is needed, eg it can be used on a waistband or on shoes.

Adapting fastenings where there is tension

Where tension is a problem, fastenings are more difficult to manage with one hand or when the grip of both hands is weak. Replace or adapt existing fastenings so that the two sides can be brought together and closed more easily. Examples are:

- *top button at neck* - sew on with elastic thread;

- *bras and corsets* - attach a Velcro cynch fastening or Kempner fastener to anchor the garment before doing up the rest of the fastening. The pull should be towards the functional hand;

- *skirt and trouser waistbands* - replace waistband fastening with Velcro cynch for those using one hand. For those with enough power in the weaker arm to hold the garment in place, try a large button, a hook and bar or a strip of Velcro.

  A loop of elastic on the end of the waistband with a button or a sideways zip are other alternatives.

  Where grip is poor in both hands, loops may be useful to help slide a hook over a bar (see p.30);

- *suspenders* - fasten the suspender to the stocking first, then attach it to the corset or suspender belt (see p.74).

Adapting garments for easier dressing

These adaptations can be used if the wearer has:

1. the use of only one hand;

2. weak grip or grasp;

3. limited use of upper or lower arms;

4. only partial use of hands.

People and their helpers, professional and at home, will need to look at the various options and try them out to see which, if any, will be most helpful. For fuller descriptions of how to carry out the adaptations, see *Clothes sense* (see inside back cover).

Underwear

- Replace straps with elastic.
- Open shoulder straps and fasten with a button and loop.
- Open both sides to open flat, fasten with press studs or Velcro dabs.
- Following an amputation, a sleeve may be cut and/or stitched to form a close-fitting stump cover.

Underpants for men

- Attach pants to waistband of trousers with Velcro dabs.
- Adapt to drop front or drop back by opening sides and add Velcro dabs to correspond with trousers.

Knickers and pants for women

- Make open crotch knickers by removing gusset.
- Open-front style for double amputee transferring forward onto toilet, leaving pants behind, or for assisted dressing.

Bras

- Replace hooks and eyes with loops and buttons.
- Replace the fastenings of a front-fastening bra with a zip 5-7cms longer than the opening. (To anchor the zip when closing it, add an elastic loop to the end and a button on a lower garment.)
- Add a cynch or Kempner fastener (p.12) to the fabric of a front-fastening midi or long length bra to anchor it, enabling the rest of the fastenings to be done up.

Corsets

- Insert or extend zip to below the bottom hem.
- Insert a second zip on the other side, opening the opposite way.

Petticoats

- Open centre front to below waist, add fastenings.

- Replace shoulder straps with elastic.

Waist slips

- Attach to skirt with Velcro dabs to simplify dressing.

Outerwear

Shirts and blouses

- Sew top and cuff buttons with elastic thread.

- Change buttons for Velcro dabs.

- Open back seam and fasten with Velcro dabs to help someone with stiff shoulders to dress.

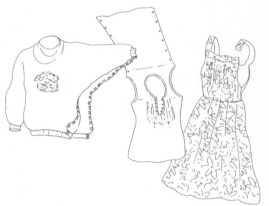

- Open under-arm and sleeve seams to open flat.

- Attach slip or pants to make a combination garment.

Trousers

- Alter waist fastenings.

- Insert zip into inner leg seam for access to urinary appliance, or outer leg seam to pull over a boot or caliper.

- Open side seams and insert full-length zips.

- Open bottom of pocket for easy access to high-release caliper.

- Drop-back and drop-front trousers

- Extend fly to crotch seam to make using urinal easier.

- Open crotch seam on either side of fly seam, add zips for easier access when using a hoist.

- Lengthen back seam and shorten front seam to make wheelchair trousers.

Jackets

- Change buttons for Velcro dabs.

- Open back seam for those with restricted shoulder and arm

movements, fastening with a long strip of Velcro.

- Open one or both side and sleeve seams for easier dressing, fastening with zip(s).
- Insert a zip into the sleeve to take an enlarged or misshapen hand (zip should open downwards).

Skirts

- Adapt waistband fastening.
- Lengthen zip to assist dressing.
- Adapt a full skirt to a wrap-over skirt.
- Make a false pocket for access to

high-release caliper.

Knitwear

- Add a slippery lining with similar stretch properties to the garment.

Dresses

- Extend front seam to below the waist.
- Insert zips into raglan sleeves seams to help dress someone who cannot lift or straighten arms.

Footwear

- Most lace-up and buckled shoes and zippered slippers can be adapted by using Velcro to accommodate swelling.
- Add loops to backs of slippers.
- Change laceholes to ski-hooks for easier fastening.

Outdoor wear

Coats

- For a wheelchair user who prefers a long coat, open the side seams and cut the back to seat length.

- For additional warmth, sew knitted cuffs to the lining inside sleeves.
- Open sleeve and insert downward opening zip to pull over enlarged or misshapen hand.

Accessories

Ties

- Tie a tie and cut it 5cm above the knot. Sew a length of elastic to each cut end to form loop to pull over head with one hand.
- Sew a loop onto the back of the narrow end - a paralysed hand can be placed in it to steady the rest of the tie while it is being tied.

4. BUYING NEW CLOTHES

It is often difficult, especially for people with restricted mobilty, to go shopping for clothes.

The following problems are often encountered by elderly and disabled people:

- many shops have steps and/or no lifts to the upper floors;

- few shops have chairs to sit on and rest;

- the racks of clothes may be so close together that it is difficult to negotiate the space with walking equipment or if you are in a wheelchair;

- the changing rooms may be small, difficult to get at, have insufficient space for the carer, or one room may be common to all;

- the shop may not have your size in stock when you get there and may be reluctant to order it for you.

Of course, not all stores are like this: many are accessible, and a large number not only have very helpful staff who will bring suitable clothes to you, but also operate a money-back guarantee so that you can take them home to try on.

It may be a good idea to phone beforehand to find out the best time to visit the store, and whether a member of staff will be available to assist you.

Only by trial and error and through other people's recommendations will you discover which shops are the most accessible, have the most helpful staff and stock the styles you like. You may wish to consider buying slightly more expensive clothes if you get good service at a particular shop.

Having someone else to buy clothes for you can be the answer to some problems, but he/she may find it difficult to choose the right garment. Underwear and hosiery are usually the easiest items to buy for someone else.

If you do discover a garment which is the correct style, size, and colour for you, try and buy another - it may not be there the next time you go shopping.

For people with limited mobility, buying by mail order may be the best solution. You can then try on the items at leisure in the privacy of your own home, but remember that the clothes will have to be sent back via a Post Office if they are unsatisfactory.

Many different catalogues are now available, most of them advertised in magazines, newspapers, mailshots, the colour supplements, disability journals and magazines for elderly people. There are also a number of specialist catalogues that take into account individual needs and indicate the easy-clothing features of each garment, helping you to choose the clothes that are right for you. If you find it difficult to know which company to deal with, bear the following points in mind:

- does the catalogue include clothing for men and women with individual needs?
- the size of the catalogue - some are very heavy (although the larger ones obviously carry a wide range of goods);
- some companies will only invoice you after you have received the goods, and many have a free return service;
- some of the smaller firms which cannot afford to invoice you, offer a prompt return of money or a free return goods service. (Cash on delivery - COD - is now used rarely.)

Shoes are probably the most difficult item to buy through mail order, as they must be the right size; however, it is often the only way to get suitable shoes. Look for a catalogue that contains a comprehensive range of footwear in an extensive range of styles.

5. TOILETING

Clothes can be a real hindrance during toileting activities! The required sequence of movement is quite complex; it often involves partial undressing, followed by strategic positioning not only to prevent the clothes being soiled, but also to keep them within easy reach so that, when ready, you can dress again!

All this, combined with factors such as the desire for privacy, the lack of space, the need to balance, and often great urgency, make toileting one of the most difficult dressing environments.

INDEPENDENT TOILETING

Standing

A man usually stands in a balanced position and needs the use of at least one hand to cope with the fly fastenings of trousers and pants. A man with poor balance will therefore need the use of two hands, the second to hold onto a rail or similar support. With the use of only one hand, a man will require good standing balance.

Sitting

In certain circumstances, it may be easier to use one of the many hand-held urinals that are now available on the market. This can be used while in a chair or bed. To remove one of the standard 'bottle' urinals, an upward movement is needed to avoid the fly and this can cause spillage. Although an extension of the fly to the crotch seam in trousers and pyjamas should avoid this, it may be worth fitting a non-spill adapter into the neck of the bottle as an added precaution.

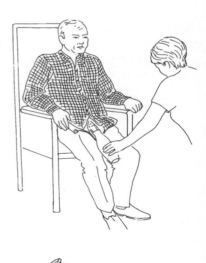

In order to sit down comfortably to use the toilet, a person must have some degree of balance and the ability to bend his/her hips. Correctly positioned wall-fixed grab rails may be invaluable. Again, as clothes will have to be

removed or adjusted, hand and/or finger movement is required.

People with stiff hips will find sitting on, and rising, from the WC easier if the seat is raised and/or there is a rail. It is best not to let garments slip below the knees. Keeping both knees slightly bent helps to prevent this happening.

For someone with weak hands

Someone with weak hands will find it difficult to manipulate and hold onto his/her clothes. However, this can be countered by various techniques, gadgets, types of clothes and adaptations.

Helpful techniques include:

- before standing up, bring garments as high up the thighs as possible;

- waistbands with firm elastic will stay at mid-thigh level if the knees are kept slightly apart;

- clothes can be:
    - held in the teeth or under the chin;
    - pushed aside using the hand as a hook;

- tucked into a waistband or belt;
- anchored by a paralysed arm.

Helpful types of clothes include:

- long underpants with loops on the waistband for braces to let trousers and pants down together;
- open crotch knickers with similar tights or stockings.

Helpful adaptations include:

- lining skirts to reduce the number of garments to be removed;
- attaching underpants to trousers with Velcro so that they can be let down together.

For a wheelchair user

A wheelchair user needs plenty of space to transfer directly onto the toilet. Designated 'wheelchair accessible toilets' should also have a range of strategically placed rails to provide assistance.

Where there is insufficient space, it may be acceptable for a wheelchair user, or someone with poor balance, to transfer onto a sanichair. This is a mobile chair with an aperture or hinged toilet seat which is designed to be used over a toilet. Some models have self propelling wheels.

Garments should only be pushed down as far as is hygienically necessary so that they are easier to pull up.

Gadgets to help with toileting

- A dressing stick to bring the hem of a skirt to hand level.
- A pick-up stick to pick up clothes which have fallen to the floor.

Braces or loops left over the arms to keep trousers from falling.

ASSISTED TOILETING

For a variety of reasons, some people will require assistance to use the toilet. They can be helped in one of three ways: standing, sitting in a sanichair or wheelchair, or in a hoist.

Standing

Some people are able to stand if they can lean against a wall or hold onto a handrail for support. However, they then have no 'free' hands with which to adjust their clothes and will therefore need the assistance of another person to do this for them. The nearer the handrail is to the toilet the better, as fewer foot movements are then needed. Drop-back trousers enable the wearer to keep hold of them.

If more than minimal assistance is needed to guide the person onto the toilet, then using a hoist should be considered. Moving the weight of the person, combined with the poor posture that often has to be adopted in cramped toilets, puts the helper at great risk of back injury.

Sitting

It may be convenient for someone to transfer onto a sanichair (see p.44). The person can transfer onto the chair outside the WC cubicle where there is more space to manoeuvre. However, where this is impractical or unsuitable, the person can be assisted from his/her wheelchair onto the toilet.

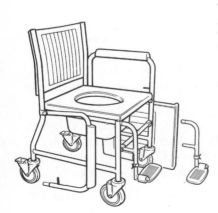

Try to move as many garments as possible before transferring:

* a wrap-around skirt can be left on the chair;

* open-crotch pants or garments that unfasten at the crotch will not have to be removed;

* men may find it easier to wear pants which can be pushed down easily under drop-back trousers. Otherwise, pants will also need to be adapted to drop-back.

In a hoist

In the past, garments always had to be adjusted before the sling(s) was positioned. In recent years, the hoist companies have put a lot of time and effort into minimising or solving the problem. There is still no universal answer, but the following alternatives are now available.

Toileting/access/ independence sling

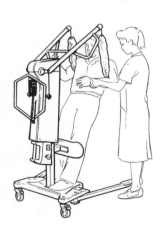

This sling can be used by people who have some muscle tone in the upper half of their body and are co-operative. It can be easily positioned while the person is in either a sitting or a lying position, and leaves good access around the person's bottom for toileting, washing, repositioning of clothes etc.

Toileting hoist

This is used mainly in hospitals or residential establishments because of its large size. It is best used with people who can carry some weight through their legs. The narrow, padded sheepskin sling is positioned under the arms, halfway down the back.

The person can quickly and easily be raised from a seated position, his/her clothes adjusted and then quickly manoeuvred onto the toilet or commode.

Unfortunately, people who need the greater amount of support offered by hammock slings and some divided leg slings will still need to have their clothing adjusted before the sling is put on.

The following clothing/adaptations may be useful when using any type of sling:

- women may find crotchless knickers easiest with a wrap-around skirt;
- men may find opening the crotch seam of the trousers and/or inserting a longer zip may help.

REDUCING URGENCY PROBLEMS

People who have urgency problems can help to reduce them by wearing:

1. the minimum of fastenings:

- open-back garments with crotchless knickers;
- elastic waisted trousers or skirts;

2. the minimum of garments:

- replace petticoats with lined garments;
- take two garments off together;

3. looser garments;

4. clothes for quick undressing:

- open-back skirts and petticoats;
- open-crotch pants or loose pants which are easy to push down (french knickers, silky non-static fabric);
- elastic waisted trousers with underpants attached;
- trouser zip replaced with Velcro;
- drop-front or drop-back trousers with pants to match;
- extended fly front opening.

DLF leaflets CC1 and CC2 contain other hints on suitable clothing.

REDUCING CONTINENCE DIFFICULTIES

Useful clothing

A great deal of time can be spent changing clothes, so some research into which type of clothing is best may be worthwhile. For instance, tight garments take longer to remove when wet.

The following types of clothing may be useful:

- separates for women, open back skirt (from the waist);

- liberty bodice or a narrow suspender belt for stockings (stockings or suspender tights are more suitable than tights);

- 'shortie' nightdresses worn with pants;

- elastic waisted trousers and pyjama trousers;

- shirts with shortened tails, sports shirts and sweaters;

- well fitting protective garments.

Continence equipment

Many different appliances are now available to help people with continence problems. However, it is essential that professional advice is sought before you buy a piece of equipment, as each person will require a different size or type. This advice could be sought from a local nurse continence adviser, from one of the larger chemists (surgical suppliers have appliance experts and fitting rooms) or from the Continence Foundation (Basement, 2D Doughty Street, London WC1N 2PH).

Some people using a catheter or a penile sheath with a urinal bag should consider the following:

- the catheter or sheath should fit well so that no leakage occurs. Where it cannot be avoided, some padding may be needed to absorb it;

- leakage occurs if the catheter is kinked, so it is important to ensure that the catheter is free and correctly placed.

The urine bag is normally strapped to the leg in a convenient place, and hidden by trousers or a long skirt. Short skirts or petticoats with a concealed bag are available. To empty the bag without removing the trousers, a zip can be sewn into the inner leg seam.

If an ostomy bag is worn, clothing should be easily removable so that it can be emptied quickly. To assist, women may find it easier to wear short or midi-line bras and waist petticoats; corsets should be made with the supports avoiding the stoma - some may prefer a hole made in the corset around the stoma; tights or stretch pants can prevent the bag from slipping should it become detached. Men may find that high waisted trousers are more comfortable and a few may prefer trousers with larger waists worn with braces.

6. TEMPORARY DISABILITIES

Most people, at some time in their lives, are liable to have a temporary disability which will affect the way they dress or the clothes they wear. This section attempts to indicate what dressing techniques are likely to help people in this situation and any temporary clothing adaptations that may help.

PLASTER CASTS

If you are required to wear a plaster cast for some weeks or even months, there are three main problems as far as dressing is concerned.

1. Plaster enlarges the limb or part of the body it encases.

2. It immobilises at least one joint.

3. It tends to be heavy.

The following are useful hints depending on which part of the body is affected.

Wrist, arm

- You are usually encouraged to use your fingers, so fastenings should be no problem.
- Dress/undress arm first/last.
- Use one-handed dressing techniques for garments for the lower body.
- Wear larger sleeved blouses and sweatshirts, short sleeves, blousons.
- If the sleeve of a suit jacket does not go over the plaster, the answer may be to borrow a suit from a friend who takes a large size. If that is not possible, the only alternative is to open the seam under the arm and add a gusset of a similar material as far as the elbow/shoulder.
- Leave shirt cuffs undone.
- Wear slip-on shoes, or use elastic laces to avoid tying knots.

Leg, ankle, knee

- Dress/undress the leg first/last.

- With a walking plaster, keep feet warm by covering toes with a sock. Drop sock onto foot with walking stick or pick-up stick, use sticks or other foot to help to manoeuvre it on.

- Wear shorts or pants with legs wide enough to go over plaster. If they are not, part open side seams.

- Trousers with wide bottoms, zipped ankle track-suit bottoms will provide enough cover; as will a skirt or kilt.

- Wear socks without elastic in tops.

Body

- If the body plaster cannot be removed at night or you are not allowed to bend to put garments over your feet, use loop ladders/braces, sock/stocking gutters, slip-on shoes.

- All clothes need to be larger than the person wears normally or very stretchy - eg ribbed jumpers; this does not apply to pants if it is possible to move slips or mini-briefs for toileting; it does apply to outdoor coats.

- Elastic waisted skirts/trousers/tracksuit bottoms may help.

- A T-shirt without seams is the easiest to wear underneath the plaster, although some women may manage with a cotton body with pants over the top (any garment under the plaster should have a high neck and short sleeves). Long vests which are longer at the sides are also available.

- It may be possible to put socks on by bringing the feet back towards the hips.

'Broomstick' plasters (for children)

- A child still in nappies will have to wear side opening pants for toileting.

- Boys will find shorts easier to wear, but they will need to be adapted. Take a pair he has grown out of, open the back seam, then along the gusset as far as the leg opening on both sides. If there is no gusset, cut across to the legs before the back seam starts to curve. The shorts can then be laid on top of the plaster. Keep the waistband together with a piece of elastic fastened on one side with a button and loop. Tuck flap underneath plaster.

Spinal fusion plaster jacket

These jackets are usually put onto teenagers who will, usually, have to be helped to dress.

- Back opening shirts and drop-back trousers with pants to match will be easiest.

Shoulder stabilisation plaster

- One-handed method of dressing will need to be adopted.

- Elastic-waisted garments are the easiest to put on.

- If you need to keep warm, wear sleeveless garments.

- If the arm is held next to the body, choose large stretchy garments, eg T-shirts, sweatshirts and always tuck the sleeve inside the garment.

- If the shoulder is braced, dress/undress limb first/last.

- Well-fitting coats cannot be worn

BURNS

If you have been burnt, dressing techniques will depend on where the burns are.

Hands

- Use grip and grasp movements.

Wrist, elbow, shoulder.

- Use one-handed techniques.

Hips, knees, ankles

- Use minimal grip techniques (see p.67 and 69).

- When pressure garments are taken off, scar tissue will be very sensitive, so wear light-weight natural fibres, such as silk or cotton, smooth fabrics and weaves next to the skin (no wool).

Sunburn

- Wear lightweight fabrics to cover you when in the sun.

JOINT REPLACEMENTS

Again, dressing techniques will depend on which joint is involved.

Single hip

- Dress/undress limb first/last.
- Bend over as little as possible.

Use stocking/sock gutter for hosiery, also a pick-up stick.

- Put lower garments on sitting down, using one hand.
- Wear slip-on shoes.
- Do not cross your legs.

Both hips

- Use the same equipment as for one hip, and braces/loop ladder for trousers.

Knees

- Dress/undress limb first/last.
- Socks rather than stockings should be worn until the swelling goes down.

Fingers

- Adopt one-handed dressing techniques with some help from affected hand.

Wrist, elbow, shoulder

- Dress/undress limb first/last.
- Dress using one-handed techniques until you are able to use new joint to help.

BACK PAIN, SCIATICA

- Find dressing techniques which involve the minimum amount of movement and no twisting.
- If you have exercises to do, see if you can combine them with dressing.
- Lie flat or stand to dress.
- Use stocking gutter for hosiery.
- Wear slip-on shoes or ones with elastic laces and use a long handled shoehorn.
- Garments should be easy to remove.
- Wear a larger size if possible, with front fastenings.

SHINGLES

The line of spots showing the site of infection is usually intensely irritating, sensitive and tender. You will feel most comfortable if no clothing touches it, but this is rarely possible. Smooth weave fabrics, such as silk and fine cotton, to cover the line will be the easiest to bear - a silk scarf may be enough. Try to keep the rest of your clothes away from the spots as far as possible.

Round waist

- Wear hipster trousers, slips or mini-briefs.

- Shirts, blouses should be worn outside trousers.

- Choose dresses without waists or belts, or dungarees.

- Loose fitting elastic waisted skirts may help.

Bra area

- It is easier not to wear a bra at all; if it is more comfortable, wear an old one which has lost most of its elasticity, or a sleep bra or a crop top if you have one.

Hips, thighs

- Wear french knickers, boxer shorts, hold-up stockings or socks, lined long skirt, baggy trousers.

- Avoid suspender belts and corsets.

WHIPLASH INJURY

If you have a whiplash injury, try to avoid twisting your neck.

- It is probably best to sit down to dress.

- Use dressing as an exercise, if exercise is allowed.

- Wear open-neck blouses or shirts to make room for the surgical collar and a scarf or cravat to cover.

- Choose front-fastening garments, not tight jumpers or polonecks.

ASTHMA

- People who have asthma should wear easily opened necks/collars to enable them to breathe more easily should an attack occur.

SHORT-TERM MEMORY LOSS

- Always follow the same pattern of dressing and undressing with the garments that are usually worn.

TRANSIENT STROKES

- Use one-handed dressing methods.
- Choose easy-to-wear garments.

DRESSING TECHNIQUES

Clothes can be put on and taken off in many different ways. Each of us has to work out which way suits us best. However, the basic ways are very similar, and these are described in this chapter.

It is divided into two main sections. The first covers dressing and undressing yourself; the second, dressing and undressing with help.

The techniques are described according to the type of garment. The same order is used throughout.

Garments for upper body:

> over the head
>
> front opening
>
> back opening

Garments for lower body:

> over the feet
>
> wrap around (open flat)

Dresses, full-length coats etc:

> over the head
>
> front opening
>
> back opening

Hosiery

Footwear

Miscellaneous garments.

Descriptions of each technique

Each description consists of an illustration and a written text. Removing and replacing a garment involves many movements, but in the space available, only one, two, or at the most three, can be illustrated in this book. Each individual can build on these basic descriptions as he/she develops his/her own methods.

The text relating to each illustration is divided as follows:

- type of garment;
- name of method;
- positions in which the activity can be carried out;

- equipment;
- description of garments as relevant;
- description of method:
  - positioning of garment
  - how method is carried out
  - any other garment for which the method can be used; variations of method; modifications of garments.

The most common methods have been included. Some involve more active movements than others in the hope that this will encourage people to experiment. One-handed methods and methods suitable for those with little strength in their upper limbs and/or grip are described, as are the ways in which grip and grasp can be used. Helpful suggestions on how to cope with spasm are also included.

General principles

1. Each person needs to discover the easiest and/or least painful ways of putting on and taking off each type of garment (see Assessing the ability to dress, Appendix 2). A therapist may be able to suggest ways of reducing or eliminating pain or spasm.

2. Support should always be within reach.

3. Encourage choice of garment and experimentation with different colours, styles and fabrics.

4. Those who need help to dress should make whatever contribution they can.

5. Positions for dressing can be changed for different garments - standing, sitting and lying down (a changing mat, plinth or floor for a child, a bed or couch for an adult), depending on which position is most convenient.

6. The weaker/affected limb should be dressed first and undressed last.

7. Surgical corsets and elastic and compression hosiery should be put on before you get up.

8. Calipers should be put on before you stand up, and artificial limbs should be dressed before being attached.

9. Keep hair out of the way.

10. If garment seams are placed correctly as clothes are put on, there

will be no need to re-adjust the clothes afterwards which may be painful and take time.

PART 1 - DRESSING AND UNDRESSING YOURSELF

Before embarking on the main text, the importance of grasp, spasm, and rolling from side to side are emphasised.

Grip and grasp

When someone's grip has been weakened by conditions such as arthritis or tetraplegia, all the different ways of using grip become important, for example, using the heel of the hand or using both hands together.

Some degree of spasm in the wrist or hand, if it can be triggered at the right time, can enhance the ability to grasp.

The ability to lift things can be improved by stabilizing the elbows on a firm surface, by using both hands together, or by using the stronger hand as a lever beneath a passive hand, eg interlinking the fingers.

Spasm

Many disabilities exhibit spasm as a symptom. It can cause pain, delay, or inhibit the carrying out an of activity. In a child with cerebral palsy, for instance, it can counteract the training he/she is receiving to control abnormal movements. Spasm in limbs can be relieved by rotating or shaking the limb, or compression through a joint. Body spasm can be reduced by bending forwards and breathing deeply.

When spasm is a result of sensitivity to touch, stretching a limb before starting an activity may be helpful. This is based on the principle that the more the body is touched, the less sensitive it becomes, resulting in a reduction in spasm.

The extension spasm of a child with cerebral palsy or an adult with a spinal injury for example, can be relieved by crossing his arms and bending him forward from the hips.

As a last resort, anti-spasmodic drugs can be given some time before the start of an activity. A period of time elapses before any drug becomes effective. Therefore, consult the person's doctor who can advise on when to take the medication.

Techniques for moving garments over the hips

Getting a garment over the hips by rolling

Positions - sitting and lying.

a. Bring garment down to waist level/up to hips.

b. Roll onto one side, ie transfer weight from one buttock to the other. Move garment as far possible up/down.

Roll onto other side. Repeat.

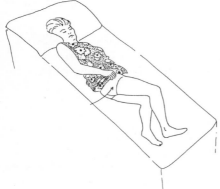

When *lying*, crossing the knees in the direction you are going helps you to roll more easily. It may be necessary to repeat this if the garment is thick or difficult to move.

c. *(sitting)* Use chair with arms. Roll from side to side, as above, using the arms of the chair as support, and bracing one foot on the floor.

Getting a garment over the hips by bridging

Position - lying.

a. Lie on back. Pull garment up to hip level or down to waist level.

b. Bend knees, dig feet into supporting surface, and raise hips. Move garment up or down into the required position.

SECTION 1 - DRESSING YOURSELF

Garments for upper body

Over the head

These garments have few or no fastenings at the neck. The neck opening needs to be large enough to go over the head without difficulty. Those people whose balance is affected when their faces are covered may find that this method will not suit them. All these methods can be used for front-fastening garments which have been partially fastened.

First method - head first, followed by arms

Positions - standing and sitting.

Fabric - stretchy.

a. Pull garment over head. Put first arm into sleeve. Arrange shoulder and sleeve seams correctly. Repeat for second arm. Pull down back of garment. Arrange seams.

b. *(sitting)* Put elbows onto chair arms to reduce shoulder movement

Second method - arms then head

Positions - standing and sitting.

Fabric - stretchy.

a. Thread both arms into sleeves as far as possible, straighten sleeve seams. Gather back of garment in hands, raise arms, bring garment over head, lift head, pull garment down. Arrange seams.

b. Can be used for a no-fastening bra or crop top. Can also be done one handed. Weaker arm should be dressed first.

Third method - first arm, over the head, second arm

Position - standing and sitting.

Fabric - stretchy.

a. Thread first arm into sleeve as far as possible. Straighten sleeve and shoulder seams. Gather back of garment in hands and bring it over head. Put second arm in. Straighten seam. Pull garment down.

b. Use chair arm to support elbow. Can also be done one handed. Weaker arm should be dressed first.

One-handed method - head first, then arms

Position - sitting.

Fabric - stretchy or one size larger.

a. Support weaker arm on lap, pillow, chair arm or table. Place garment downwards, neck opening away from body.

b. Pick up garment at hem. Gather body of garment in hand as far as neck if this is helpful. Pull over head.

Place weaker arm in sleeve first and pull over and adjust.

Put second arm in, pushing sleeve downwards against body. Pull down at back.

c. Long sleeves on stronger arm should have cuffs either with no fastening, eg elasticated or ribbed, or be already fastened.

Front opening

First method - first arm in, garment brought round neck, second arm in

Positions - standing or sitting.

Equipment - dressing stick, or pick-up stick.

a. Hold garment by shoulder above sleeve to be put on first.

b. Thread first sleeve on as far as neck. Straighten seams. (If unable to reach behind the neck to pull the garment towards the other shoulder, a *dressing stick* can be used. Put second arm into armhole, settle sleeves. Fasten.

c. A garment with some fullness at back makes pulling on second sleeve easier. A slippery lining on an outer garment is easier to put on. When doing up fastening where co-ordination is impaired, use a mirror to start the fastening process at the bottom and work up. Make into an over-the-head garment by fastening at the bottom.

Second method - garment on chair, put in both arms together

Positions - standing and sitting.

Equipment - dressing stick.

a. *(standing)* Place garment inside out over back of high chair, stand behind as illustrated.

   (sitting) Place garment inside out over front of chair, pushing any free fabric to back of chair seat.

b. *(standing)* Bend knees slightly, put arms into sleeves.

   (sitting) Sit down on front of chair, put arms into sleeves. Use opposite hands to bring up onto shoulders.
Settle sleeves on shoulders
   using *dressing stick* to help bring garment up.

c. This method can be used with one hand.

Third method - sleeves on, raise arms

Positions - standing and sitting.

Fabric - stretchy, lined or larger size garment.

a. Place garment inside out, collar nearest body - on lap if *sitting*, on table or chair if *standing*.

b. Put arms into sleeves above elbows. Raise arms to bring garment over head. Allow sleeves to slip down arms. Bend head to adjust garment.

Fourth method - swing round shoulders

Positions - standing and sitting.

a. Hold garment by front of collar or neckband

b. Swing round, settle safely on shoulders. Let go of one side, put arm into sleeve on that side; put second sleeve on. Fasten. (If *sitting*, lean forward before swinging garment round to prevent the chair back being included.)

c. Easy method for cape.

One-handed method

Positions - standing and sitting.

Fabric - stretchy.

a. Put sleeve onto weaker arm. Pull up on shoulder as high as possible. Straighten seams. Rest of garment should hang down centre back.

b. Shrug shoulders; with stronger hand reach behind neck and bring garment round across back and onto shoulder. Put arm into sleeve, adjust and fasten.

c. Difficult if armhole is very tight.
   A gusset can be put in under the arm.

Back opening

First method - draw sleeves on

Positions - standing and sitting.

a. Hold garment by shoulder,
   above sleeve to be put on first

b. Guide onto arm, straighten
   shoulder seam. Put second sleeve
   into armhole. Fasten by doing up
   top button first, gathering up
   garment as far as second button
   and fastening etc until unable to
   fasten any more. Any further
   buttons will need to be fastened at
   waist level.

c. Some help may be required with
   fastenings. Method can be used
   for full-length open-back garment.

d. People with short arms may have
   difficulty with back fastenings.

Second method - fastening at the front, swinging round to the back

Positions - standing, sitting and
lying down.

Equipment - dressing stick.

Elasticated straps essential for
this method.

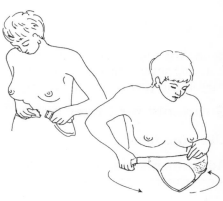

1 a. Bring bra round body at
       waist level. Make sure the
       cups are correctly
       positioned.

       If *lying*, use *dressing
       stick* to push garment
       under body.

b. Fasten and swing round to the back. Put arms into straps, pull straps onto shoulders, using *dressing stick* if required.

c. *(lying)* Most people have a natural hollow at waist level which makes it easier to push a bra underneath. Broad straps stay more easily on shoulders. Elastic straps can be used to anchor otherstraps by tucking them underneath.

2 - as for 1 but one-handed

Positions - sitting.

Equipment - dressing stick.

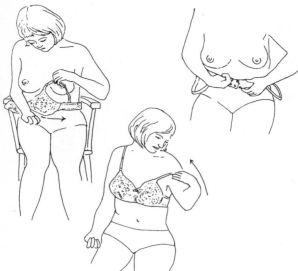

a. Bring bra round body at waist level, anchoring one side with weight of weaker hand/arm.

b. Fasten; proceed as with 1.

c. Sew fabric back under hooks for easier fastening. If it is not possible

to anchor the bra, use a front fastening bra with a Kempner or cynch fastener sewn onto bottom edge (see p.12). These, once fastened, enable the rest of the fastenings to be done up.

Garments for lower body

Over the feet

All garments with legs have to be put on feet first, which means that there must always be some way of getting the garment as far as the feet.

First method - bending from the waist

Positions - standing and sitting.

Equipment - loops/braces and dressing stick.

a. Hold garment by waistband, position correctly, and drop to floor.

b. *(standing)* Bend over and insert feet. Bring up to waist. If unable to bend to the floor, a *dressing stick* may be used or *braces/elastic loops* can be attached to trousers to provide an extended reach.

   (sitting) Bend down, put feet into each leg and bring up to knees. Holding onto waistband, either stand to pull over hips, or pull up to thighs and roll from side to side (see p.58). Fasten.

Second method - lying down enables garment to be supported

Position - lying.

Equipment - dressing stick, loops/braces, rope ladder.

a. Sit up, pick up garment by waistband and flick it forward to settle in front.

b. Draw over feet and bring it up legs as far as thighs, using *dressing stick* or *loops/braces* as required.

   Roll from side to side or bridge hips to bring over hips (see p.58), or stand to finish dressing. Fasten.

c. With painful side-hip movement, put a bandage or towel under the leg and use as a sling to move leg sideways and/or upwards.

Poor sitting balance may be helped by use of *rope ladder*; support can be given by pillows or back rest.

One-handed method

Positions - sitting then standing, or lying.

Equipment - braces/loops.

a. *(sitting)* Hold garment by waistband, and drop garment to floor. Use *braces/loops* if necessary, to maintain control over garment.

b. Insert feet, weak leg first, and bring as far as thighs.

Then *(standing)* bend and bring up to waist, using *braces/loops* to keep garment steady.

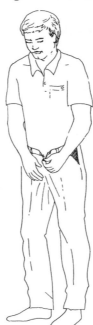

(sitting or standing) Fasten, using weak arm as an anchor.

c. Poor balance can be helped by leaning against a solid piece of furniture or wall.

Adapt waistband fastenings where necessary.

People with poor grip but flexible knees and hips

Position - lying.

Equipment - dressing stick.

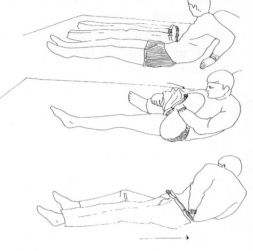

a. Put trousers (or skirt) right side up on bed beside lower half of body.

b. Lift one leg with hand on same side, ease on leg of trousers with wrist of other arm/ put leg in skirt.

   Repeat for other leg.

   Roll over on side and pull up hip.

   Repeat for other side, and fasten (see p.69).

   Using *dressing stick* as necessary.

People with poor grip and inflexible knees

Position - lying.

Equipment - loops/braces attached to waistband.

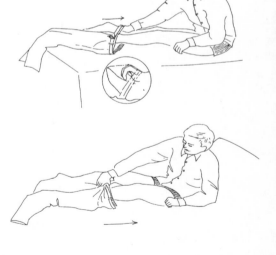

a. Place trousers at end of bed adjacent to feet.

b. Move trousers over feet and under heels (see inset), leaning on one elbow for support.

   Ease up the legs by alternately pushing garment under heels and pulling up the legs.

   Once trousers are at hip level, roll from side to side to bring them up to the waist. Fasten.

c. Crossing the feet may help to raise the heels - in this case, care must be taken to position trouser legs correctly.

Zips in the inner seams at the cuff may make trousers easier to put on. They should be undone before starting to dress - help may be needed to fasten them.

This method can be exhausting and should be practised by doing a bit at a time until it can be managed completely.

Wrap around (skirt, corset)

First method

Positions - standing.

a. Hold garment at each end of waistband.

b. Place garment on left hip. Bring garment round the back; fasten.

Second method

Position - lying.

a. Lay garment open on the bed.

b. Roll onto it; fasten.

c. Surgical corsets are best put on flat. Kempner or cynch fasteners (see p.12) are useful for people using one hand.

Third method

Position - sitting.

a. Place garment loosely in chair, inside uppermost, with sides overlapping arms of chair.

b. Sit down, pull round, fasten; adjust as necessary.

c. Can be done one-handed, with weaker/ heavier arm anchoring garment as necessary.

Fastening waistbands

First method

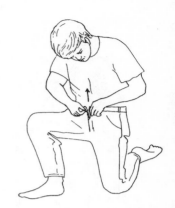

Positions - standing, sitting and lying.

Equipment - dressing stick, loops.

a. Bring ends of waistband together

b. Do up fastening.

c. Buttons may be replaced by a trouser hook and bar or by Velcro. *Loop* on end of waistband (see p.30) with trouser hook and bar, can help poor finger movement - pull *loop* so that trouser hook is well beyond the bar and then allow to slip back close to waistband.

People with poor grip or finger movement

Position - lying.

Equipment - dressing stick, loops and button hook.

a. Bring ends of waistband together, using what grip is available.

b. Fasten waistband, using *button hook* to do up buttons, heel of hand to close Velcro, *loop* to help do up hook and bar.

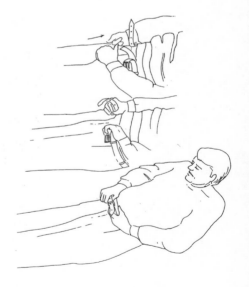

Do up zip if wearing trousers, with *dressing stick* if necessary.

c. An enlarged zip pull may be helpful.

Replace zip/waistband fastening with Velcro.

Dresses, full length coats etc

Over the head

Arms first, followed by head

Positions - standing and sitting.

Fabric - stretchy, or with good opening at side, front or back, extending below waist.

a. Gather up skirt with both hands as far as neck opening.

b. Put arms in sleeves, pulling well up onto shoulders. Elbows on table or chair arms stabilises the shoulders. Pull over head. Adjust seams.

   (standing) Skirt will drop.

   (sitting) Roll from side to side to bring skirt down. Do up any fastenings.

Front opening

First method - first arm, round body, second arm

Positions - standing or sitting.

a. Put one arm into sleeve and bring well up onto shoulder.

b. Put other hand on edge of collar.

   Swing garment round. Put second arm in sleeve while garment is still in the air. A *dressing stick* or a *pick-up stick* can be used if unable to reach behind head to pull garment around the back.

   Fasten. Stand to drop or *(sitting)* roll to pull over hips.

c. Can be done one-handed, dressing the weaker arm first.

Second method - one handed

Garment needs good-sized opening.

Position - standing.

Equipment - pick-up stick.

a. Hold up garment by shoulders, with front bodice facing.

b. Let it down until it is low enough to step into.

 (Back opening garment) raise as far as the waist, twist it round to correct position.

 Bring bodice up until arms can be put into sleeves.

 Complete dressing.

c. Leaning against the wall may give support.

 Doubling the bodice over the skirt may make the garment easier to cope with.

Half-open back

First method - body of garment, then arms

Position - sitting.

Garment should open well below waist.

a. Bring whole garment over the head and arms and drop garment to waist.

b. Insert arms into armholes, pull up to shoulders.

 Settle onto shoulders and fasten.

 Stand to allow skirt to drop or *(sitting)* roll from side to side.

Second method - feet first

Positions - standing and sitting.

Equipment - zipaid, loops.

a. Make a ring of garment to step into.

b. *(standing)* Step into garment.

  (sitting) Put feet into garment, bend over or hold onto *loops/braces* and draw up to thighs.

  Roll or *stand* to bring over hips.

  Pull up to slip over shoulders and arms.

  Settle seams.

  Fasten, using *zipaid* if necessary.

Hosiery (socks, stockings, tights)

First method

Positions - sitting and lying.

Equipment - sock or stocking aid, stool.

- *Socks, stockings*

a. Hold sock open between both thumbs, line up with foot, heel of sock underneath (illustration 1).

  One knee over the other, gather stocking up in hands as far as toe, place over toes (illustration 2).

  Double sock over itself, place on foot as far as heel (illustration 3).

b. Pull on over foot and up leg, straightening as required.

c. For stiff hips, use a *stocking aid* *(see p.28)*.

  A heel-less sock is useful where co-ordination or sight is poor.

Socks with a separate big toe are available for those people who use their feet rather than their hands.

- *Tights*

a. Put on first leg as in illustration 2 as far as knees.

b Put on second leg in same way. Smooth tights from knees as high as possible.

Stand to pull over hips.

c. Some people stand to put on their tights. Those with stiff hips can use a tights aid (see p.28).

One-handed method

Position - sitting.

Equipment - dressing stick, pick-up stick and stool.

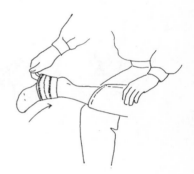

a. Cross weak leg onto stronger leg and/or place on a *stool* for support and to bring leg closer. Hold sock by toe, drop onto foot.

For stockings, place on lap, put hand inside, and work down, like a caterpillar, gathering the stocking into the hand until toe is reached. Place onto foot.

b. Smooth onto foot and up the leg, a bit at a time until top can be reached. Fasten suspenders onto stockings.

c. *Dressing stick* and *pick-up stick* can be used to drop sock/stocking onto foot and bring them upon the leg.

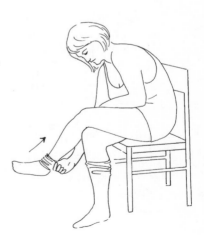

Knee-high or above-knee hosiery avoid the need for suspenders.

A stool reduces the amount of bending required.

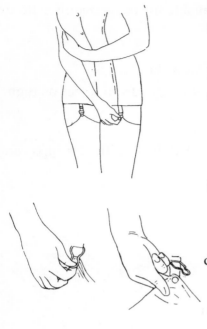

Doing up suspenders - one-handed method

Positions - standing and sitting.

a. Put on stockings and suspender belt.

   Choose position where there is no strain between the suspender and stocking welt.

b. Slip button of suspender under welt and steady it against the thigh.

   Use thumb and forefinger to bring slide over button and pull up.

c. Stay-up stockings or tights avoid the need for suspenders.

   Adapt suspenders as p.16, attach suspenders to stockings first and then fix to suspender belt.

Shoes

First method - slip-on shoe

Positions - standing and sitting.

Equipment - stool, shoehorn or shoe assist.

a. Place shoes in front of feet.

b. Ease foot into shoe, using *shoehorn*; put on second shoe.

c. Long-handled *shoehorn* minimises bending.

   The other foot can be used to fix the shoe while it is being put on, or, when *standing*, the shoe can be placed against a wall or put in a *shoe assist*.

Second method - footwear with fastenings

Positions - standing and sitting.

Equipment - shoehorn and dressing stick.

a. Put trousers, if worn, on first.

   Open out fastening.

   (sitting) Cross leg over opposite knee, or place on stool.

   (standing) Put foot up on chair, bend over or kneel down.

b. Put shoe/boot onto foot, using *shoehorn* if necessary. Fasten.

c. Boots should be put on with both hands where possible. *Standing* may be easier. A loop at the back of an ankle boot helps in pulling it on.

   Laces can be replaced with hooks or by a zip, which can be closed using a *dressing stick*. Those with poor sensation in feet should have footwear which allows the position of the toes to be checked.

One-handed method

Position - sitting.

Equipment - shoehorn and dressing stick.

a. Place shoes in front of feet, laced shoes should be undone and opened wide.

b. Place weaker foot in shoe, anchoring it by using the able foot or putting it against a firm piece of furniture. Use *shoehorn*.

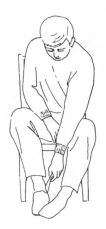

   Put other shoe on, pushing shoe against a piece of furniture if necessary. Fasten. Buckles and Velcro can be fastened with one hand; laces usually need a special technique (see below).

c. If elastic laces are used, a *shoehorn* is essential. The tongue may need to be stabilised, either by threading the lace through a hole made in the tongue, or by stitching it down one side.

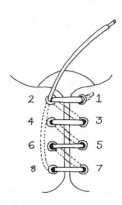

One-handed method of lacing and fastening

Equipment - dressing stick for tightening laces.

Before putting shoe on, lace shoe; remove metal tag of lace, make a knot and thread it up through 1. Thread down through 2, up through 3 and so on to 8. Thread back from 8 up through 2, leaving a long end. To fasten, tighten the lace from the top towards the toe (3-8) and then pull at long end. Make a loop, pass it over and under the top lacing and tighten.

OR Use one of the lacing aids.

Miscellaneous garments

Gloves

One-handed method

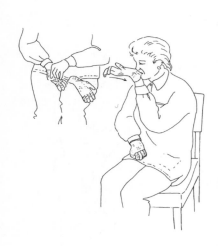

a. Place gloves on thighs, cuffs towards the body.

b. Pull glove onto weaker hand with other hand. 'Crawl' able hand into second glove, pull cuff down with the teeth.

c. Woollen or silk gloves are flexible so easier to put on. Leather gloves are less so, and need to be one size larger; lined gloves may be more difficult. Mittens are easier, a muff may be enough to keep hands warm. If teeth are always needed to pull a cuff on, the cuff may need strengthening.

SECTION 2 - UNDRESSING YOURSELF

Garments for upper body

Over the head

These garments either have a few or no fastenings at the neck. Those people whose balance is affected when their faces are covered may find that these methods do not suit them.

First method - arms out first, then over the head

Positions - standing, sitting and lying.

Fabric - stretchy (or good neck opening).

a. Undo any fastenings.

   Take off sleeves singly, from the armhole, pulling elbow back.

b. Bend head forward.

   Gather body of garment in hands and lift quickly over head (towards back)

   (sitting) Chair arms may support elbows.

c. If *sitting*, always sit well back in chair.

Second method - cross arms, bring garments over the head

Positions - standing and sitting.

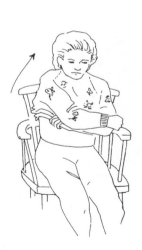

a. Undo any fastening.

   Cross arms, take hem of garment in each hand.

b. Bring garment up over the shoulders and head, keeping arms crossed until garment is clear of the head.

   Let go of garment, hold cuffs and pull off sleeves.

c. Use for long petticoats, nightdresses, dresses which cannot be dropped to the floor.

Third method - bring garments over the head, then arms

Positions - standing and sitting.

Fabric - stretchy garment, or slippery garment easiest.

a. Undo any fastenings.

Grasp sides of neck of garment in each hand.

b. Lean forward.

Bring body of garment right over head. Pull off sleeves from cuff.

c. *(sitting)* Put elbows on table or chair arms.

Gather up back of garment before bringing over the head.

Always sit well back in the chair when seated.

One-handed methods

Position - sitting.

Fabric - stretchy.

1 a. Place weaker arm on lap or a pillow placed on a table or chair arm. Bend head forward. Hold garment at the back of the collar.

b. Gather up body of garment at back. Pull over head. Ease sleeve off stronger arm by moving it against body, or using the teeth. Remove sleeve from weaker arm.

2 a. Grasp cuff on able side with able hand. Bring hand up inside sleeve, using body where necessary.

b. Gather up side of garment. Bring garment over the head; undress the weaker arm.

Front opening

These garments include shirts, blouses, jackets, liberty bodices, cardigans.

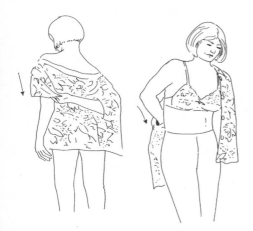

First method - slip garment off from the back

Position - standing.

a. Ease garment off shoulders by pulling on front bands and shrugging shoulders.

b. Put hands behind body, pull one sleeve off with opposite hand; garment will now be at side of body; take other sleeve off.

OR Let sleeves fall as far as elbows; bring arms to front, pull sleeves off one at a time.

Second method - ease sleeves off from armhole

Position - sitting.

a. Ease one sleeve off arm from armhole as far as elbow. Take rest of arm out.

b. Hold collar on the same side, swing garment round the back, remove from other arm.

c. Once one sleeve has been removed, the other can be taken out and the garment left on the chair.

Third method - pulling over the head

Positions - standing and sitting.

a. Undo fastenings. Grasp shoulders of garment with both hands.

b. Bend forward. Pull garment over

head, then remove arms from sleeves.

c. Can be done with one hand, by grasping garment at back of neck.

Fourth method - pull garment from front bands

Positions - standing and sitting.

Equipment - dressing stick.

a. Undo fastenings, push garment off shoulders, using *dressing stick* as required.

b. Allow sleeves to fall as far as elbows; pull sleeves off from the front.

c. Lined garment will slip off more easily.

One-handed methods

1. Collar well up on neck

Position - standing.

> a. Undo fastenings. Bring collar well up to the neck on weaker side.
>
> b. Grasp hem of garment on stronger side, pull down and sleeve should come down too. Remove sleeve from weaker arm.

2. Push off shoulders

Position - sitting.

Equipment - dressing stick.

> a. Undo fastenings. Push off shoulders of garment.
>
> b. Grasp centre of band with a stronger hand, pull backwards and downwards, thus easing off sleeve. Pull sleeve off weaker arm.
>
> c. Lined garments make this easier.

3. Pull over head

Position - sitting (see third method p.79).

Back opening

These garments include bras.

Positions - standing and sitting.

Equipment - dressing stick.

1 a. Undo fastenings by reaching round to
      the back of the neck and undoing the
      first fastening.

      Pull up the rest of the garment gradually,
      undoing fastenings as they reach the hands.

   b. Reach round back of neck with one hand for front band and
      bring to front, pulling off sleeve.

      Pull off other shoulder and sleeve.

   c. Difficult without full shoulder movement and both hands. It is
      easier to undo fastenings on these garments than to do them up.

2. For bras

   a. Undo fastenings by bending arms behind the back.

   b. Slip straps off shoulders.

   c. It may be easier to slip the straps off the shoulders (using
      dressing stick if necessary), moving the back of the bra to the
      front, and undoing the fastenings at waist level.

Garments for lower body

Over the feet

These garments include trousers, pants, shorts, culottes, divided
skirts, skirts, hosiery and footwear.

All garments with legs have to be taken off feet first, which means
that there must always be some way of getting the garment as far as
the feet. If the person is unable to bend that far, a number of
dressing gadgets can help.

Problems with tighter garments are likely because they usually need
to be rolled down. Briefs and slips can also give rise to problems as
they are tight and consequently offer little material to hang on to.

First method

Positions - standing and kneeling.

a. Undo waistband fastening if any.

b. With both hands push garment off hips then allow garment to drop off. Withdraw feet.

c. When kneeling, push garment as far as knees, then stand. Elastic waisted garments eliminate fastenings, but take a little more effort to push over hips.

Second method

Positions - standing and sitting.

Equipment - loops.

a. Undo waistband fastening if any. If you want to hang onto the garment, put *loops* round your wrists.

b. *(standing)* Push garment over hips, using *loops* and drop.

   (sitting) Push garment to waist.

   Roll to one side, bring garment over hip, and repeat for other side.

   Stand or bring up one knee or cross the knees, take the garment off.

c. *Loops* enable you to hang onto the garment instead of having to pick it up from the floor. When taking off trousers, it is usually better to take footwear off first.

Third method

Position - lying.

Equipment - dressing stick.

a. Undo waistband fastening if any.

b. Push garment to hips, roll to one side and push garment over hip; repeat for other side.

Sit up, bend knees, push garment over knees to feet, bend forward to pull it off feet, using *dressing stick* where necessary.

c. You can use the other foot to push each trouser leg off, once they are as far as the knees OR bend over to push them off.

Drop-front or drop-back trousers can eliminate the need to push garments to hips.

Zips at trouser leg bottoms make it easier to get trousers over feet - to unfasten, bend knees to bring feet nearer (see Adaptations p.37).

One-handed method

Positions - standing with support and sitting.

Equipment - loops.

a. Undo fastenings if any. Grasp garment on stronger side. Lean against support - wall, heavy chest of drawers - if necessary.

b. Push over hips or, if *sitting*, stand to allow to drop down. Use *loops* (or *braces*) to hang onto garment.

c. When taking off trousers, remove shoes first.

Method for minimal grip or grasp

Positing - lying down.

Equipment - dressing stick, loops.

Look at the methods of grip and grasp described on p.37 when unfastening or pushing garment down.

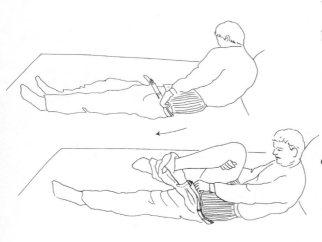

a. Undo waistband if necessary.

b. Push garment down the hips, rolling from one side to the other Raise one knee with hand, push garment down leg and off foot.

Repeat for other leg.

c. When taking off trousers, take footwear off first. Attaching pants to trousers means that both garments can be taken off together.

Drop-back or drop-front trousers eliminate need to push garment as far as the hips (see Adaptations p.37).

Those with inflexible knees will need a *dressing stick* to push trousers down.

Underwear

'Baggy' pants (eg boxer shorts, french knickers and pants without elastic round the legs) are probably the easiest to take off. They can also be attached to trousers without much difficulty so that they can be taken off together.

Smaller garments are trickier to manage. Try using a *dressing stick* to push down as far as the hips, the stretchier the fabric the better. (It will need practice.) They can then be pushed off like other garments for the lower body.

Y-fronts are probably too difficult for people who do not have enough grip.

Cami-knickers, 'teddies' and 'bodies' are normally unfastened at the crotch, and then taken off over the head as on p.77 and p.78. The normal button or poppa fastening can be replaced with Velcro dabs.

Wrap around

Corset or corselette

Positions - standing and lying.

a. Undo fastening starting at the top, one hand holding side steady.

b. *(standing)* Remove.

 (lying) Leave garment on bed.

 (corselette) Undo strap on side of fastening or bring over the head.

c. Replace hooks and eyes with Kempner, cynch or D-ring fastener to make fastening easier (see p.12 for details).

Dresses etc

These include garments with side, centre, front or back openings as far as waist, petticoats, garments without fastenings.

First method - over-the-head

Position - standing.

Fabric - stretchy.

a. Undo any fastenings. Cross arms, bend forward, grip garment at hem with hands. Gather up fabric as far as waist if this helps.

b. Pull garment up and over head, uncrossing arms. Strip off sleeves.

c. Firm necklines without fastenings may be difficult. Enlarge opening (see p.34).

Second method - drop garment to floor

Easier if openings are below the waist.

Positions - standing and sitting.

Equipment - dressing stick or zipaid.

a. Undo fastenings, if any, using *zipaid* if required.

b. Pull sleeves or straps down arms, using *dressing stick.*

(standing) Dress will slip off, step out.

(sitting) Leave garment at hip level until moving from chair, or roll from side to side to push off. (see p.58).

Hosiery (socks, stockings, tights)

Where grip or grasp is minimal, hosiery with little elasticity will be the easiest to manage.

First method - pulling on toe of sock

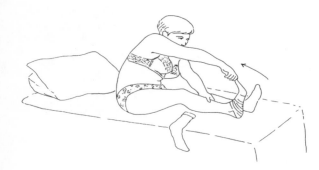

Position - sitting.

a. Remove footwear, push sock down to heel.

b. Grasp toe of sock and pull off. Repeat for other leg.

c. Bending the knees can help.

Tubular socks or socks without elasticated welt are the easiest to manage.

Second and one-handed method - one foot over other knee

Position - sitting.

Equipment - dressing stick or pick-up stick, stool.

a. Remove footwear. For stockings, undo suspenders, for tights, take down from hips, then roll down legs as far as knees.

Cross one leg over the other (using hand to lift if necessary).

b. Put hands on either side of hosiery within the welt. Push down until it comes off the foot, using the *dressing* or *pick-up stick* as an aid. Cross over the other leg and repeat for other foot.

c. Once it is over the heel, the hosiery can be pulled off by the toe. Putting the foot onto a *stool* will support the foot.

Putting hosiery on with one hand is best done by putting the foot onto a *stool* and using hosiery which is not very tight, eg socks without elasticated tops. Avoid struggling with the head bent, so make sure the *stool* is high enough or the chair is not too high.

Footwear

Footwear includes shoes and sandals with laces, buckles, zips, elastic inserts, Velcro, hooks, and slip-ons; boots with laces, buckles, zips, hooks and pull-ons; and slippers with zips, Velcro, elastic inserts and slip-ons.

First method - raising and supporting the knee

Position - standing and sitting.

Equipment - stool/chair.

a. Raise foot.

   (sitting) Put on a *stool*.

   (standing) Put the foot on a *chair*. Undo fastenings. Open shoe out well.

b. *(sitting)* Push footwear off with free hand.

(standing) Put foot to floor and slip shoe off.

c. Some people kneel to unfasten their footwear and then stand to take it off; some sit and cross their knees.

Second method - using other foot

Positions - standing, sitting and lying.

Equipment - boot remover.

a. Undo any fastenings and open shoe out.

b. Put one foot behind the other. Put toe on heel of shoe, push downwards. Repeat for other foot.

c. A *boot remover* can also be used.

PART 2 - DRESSING AND UNDRESSING WITH HELP

Some general principles for the helper

1. Use dressing as a passive exercise whenever possible.

2. The helper's movements should be firm, smooth and gentle.

3. Find out the way the person prefers to be dressed, and which movements are likely to increase or lessen pain or induce or reduce spasm.

4. Furniture should be at the correct height for the helper and be adjustable to allow easy transfer.

5. The helper will be able to use both hands if the person to be dressed is supported, but only one hand if he/she has to support limbs or head.

6. The position of the person to be dressed should be planned so that the helper is subject to the least amount of stress.

7. To save time, several garments can be put on and then adjusted together, eg pants and trousers; but this should not be done if it increases the pain or discomfort of the person being dressed.

8. Children are easier to dress than adults, because they are lighter, easier to move and generally more amenable to persuasion or distraction. As they grow heavier and develop a will of their own, however, these advantages will disappear and clothes chosen by the child which are light, easy to put on, attractive and adjustable will become more important.

Children with cerebral palsy are usually handled in a particular way when they are being dressed, helped to sit down and being carried, and they should always be moved in the same way.

Anyone who is liable to experience spasm should be handled in the ways that, from experience, have been found to reduce spasm.

SECTION 1 - DRESSING WITH HELP

Long and short garments

Over the head

First method - head first, then arms

Positions - sitting and lying.

Fabric - stretchy or half open front or back fastened garment.

a. Gather garment in hands as far as neck.

b. Put over head. Place shoulder seams correctly.

Bend the first arm at the elbow and either put person's hand into armhole and pull sleeve down arm, or thread own hand through sleeve, grasp person's hand and bring it down sleeve. Adjust seam.

Repeat with second sleeve.

Long garment - *stand* up to let garment fall over hips, or *(sitting or lying)* roll person from side to side.

c. A fixed elbow is easier to dress by second or third method described below.

Second method - arms first, then head

Positions - sitting or lying.

Fabric - stretchy, long or short garments.

a. Put arms into sleeves either by gathering up each sleeve and feeding it over the hands and arms, or put own hand down the sleeve and bring the person's arm through the sleeve.

Gather the front of the garment in the hands; lift and support the

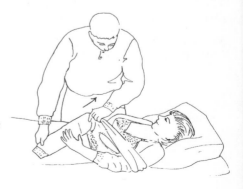

head while taking the garment over it.

(lying) Sit up or roll person to bring garment down the back.

Third method - one arm in, then over the head, then second arm

Positions - sitting, lying.

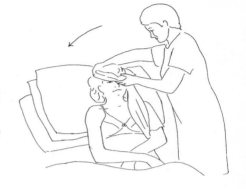

Fabric - stretchy, or good neck opening.

a. Thread first arm in (see method 1).

b. Gather garment up as far as the neck on other side, place over the head. Put in second arm. Adjust seams.

   (lying) Sit up or roll to pull garment down.

Front opening

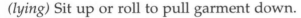

First method - first sleeve on, bring garment round back, second sleeve

Position - sitting (either on chair or bed).

a. Stand to back of person. Put first sleeve on (see method 1).

b. Bring garment high up onto shoulder. Adjust seams.

   Move to the other side. Bring round the back, raise armhole to above shoulder level.

   Bend elbow of second arm, thread into sleeve. Adjust seams. Fasten.

   OR Only feed first sleeve on as far as elbow.

Bring garment round the back, keeping second armhole as low as possible.

Turn hand round to face backwards and put it into second armhole.

Bring sleeve up arm.

c. A firm garment such as a suit jacket can be split up the back seam (see p.37) for stiff or painful shoulders. Additional fullness at the back also helps.

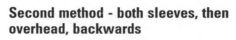

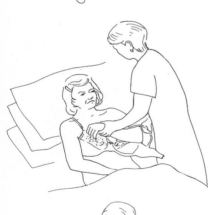

Second method - both sleeves, then overhead, backwards

Positions - sitting and lying.

Fabric - stretchy, roomy or sleeveless garment.

a. Garment placed downwards, hem to body.

b. Thread on sleeves. Support the arms. Gather garment and lift over head. Bring down back and adjust.

   (lying) Arms are supported by chest.

Back opening

Positions - sitting, lying.

a. Thread first arm on.

b. Thread second arm on.

   (lying) Roll over and fasten

   (sitting) Bend forward and fasten.

c. If more than one back-fastening garment is being put on, they should all be fastened at the same time.

Garments for lower body

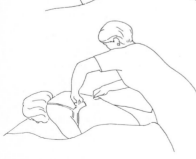

Rolling from side to side

Position - lying.

a. Ensure the head is well supported.

b. Roll person away from helper. Pull up side of garment. Roll towards helper. Pull up other side of garment.

c. Where one knee is stiff, use it as a lever to swing the body over. Rolling may be made easier if the leg which is to go underneath is straight and the leg on top is bent at the knee.

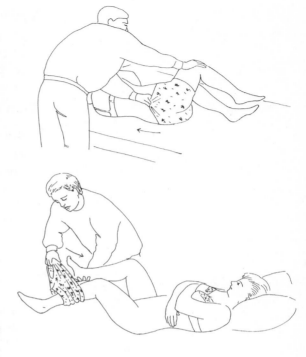

First method - brought over feet

Positions - sitting and lying (pants, trousers, skirts).

a. Put hosiery on first under trousers and skirts.

b. Thread one hand through garment leg or skirt, grasp appropriate foot and bring through. Repeat with other foot.

Draw garment up legs and over knees.

Roll from side to side to pull garment over hips or pull up when moving from bed to chair. Fasten.

c. Trousers and pants can be put on together. A zip in inner leg seam may make trousers easier to put on.

Second method - over helper's knees or carer seated behind

Position - lying (tights, trousers or pants).

a. Roll garment down as far as first foot.

b. Place foot in garment; cover person's hands and draw garment up together.

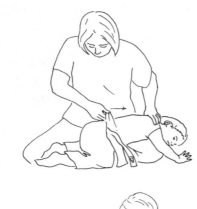

Repeat for other leg.

Move person from seated position to lean over carer's knee. Bring garment over hips. Sit up to fasten.

Wrap around

Position - lying.

a. Roll to one side. Place garment over hips, rolling rest of garment and placing it on the bed.

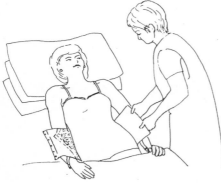

b. Roll back, pull garment straight. Bring ends together. Fasten.

c. Where a corset is not essential, a small suspender belt, which can be pushed under the back, or stay-up stockings are alternatives. Remove the back suspender or bring it to the side if the wearer is seated all day.

Dresses, full length coats etc

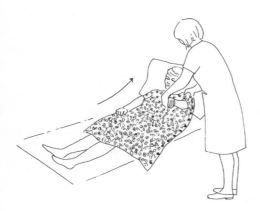

Back opening

First method

Positing - sitting, lying.

a. Place garment over person.

b. Place first arm through sleeve; tuck rest of garment well under person on same side Repeat for second arm. Roll away from carer. Straighten and pull down. Fasten.

Half-open, back or front

First method

Position - sitting.

a. Stand beside person; gather up dress in hands, with back of garment towards the back of person.

b. Put over head; bring down as far as waist.

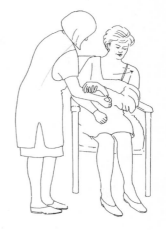

Thread first arm through sleeve, supporting arm at wrist.

Thread second arm through. Bring garment up onto shoulders.

To fasten back, lean forward.

Roll from side to side to pull garment down or stand up.

c. A half-open garment can also be put on from the feet upwards.

A wrap-around skirt enables it to be arranged round the hips without the person having to be moved.

Half-open front

Position - sitting (drop shoulder or raglan sleeves).

a. Gather garment into circle and put over head.

b. Bring garment down to waist level; bring arms out.

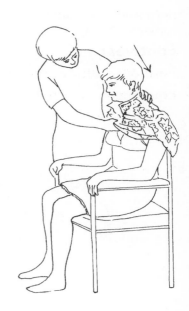

Ease arms to the back and place them in the sleeves. Bring garment up to shoulders. Adjust and fasten.

c. Zips in the sleeve seams may be helpful for those with tightly bent elbows.

Hosiery

A - Helper behind

B - Helper in front

Position - lying.

A&B a. Gather garment in hands as far as foot.

A   b. Complete as on p.93.

B   b. Guide up the leg, giving support where necessary. Fasten stockings with suspenders. (If person is seated all day, only front suspender may be necessary.)

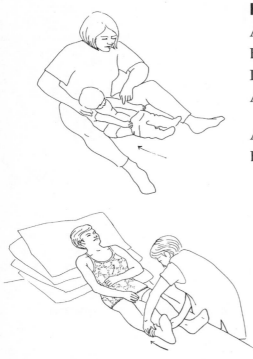

    c. Turning the foot of the garment back on itself may be easier (see p.73). Socks without heels are easy to put on. Hosiery should fit well to avoid any permanent damage. Suspenders and suspender belts may be replaced by tights/stay-up stockings/socks.

Footwear

Positions - sitting and lying.

Equipment - shoehorn.

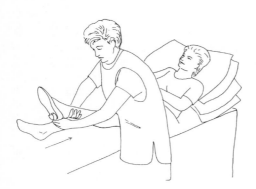

a. Open out any fastenings.

b. Support ankle with one hand, put footwear on with the other. Repeat. Put feet back on bed or stool to fasten.

c. Feet which have little sensation or are likely to be damaged easily should be placed carefully into shoes which can be opened down to the toes.

Miscellaneous garments

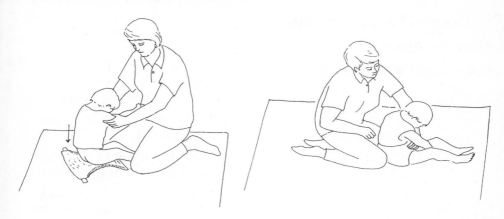

Nappies

Sitting method which prevents the child falling back

Position - lying.

a. Hold child under arms and lift.

b. Lower him onto nappy holding him between helper's knees. Turn him round or move behind him. Fold nappy round body and fasten.

SECTION 2 - UNDRESSING WITH HELP

Garments for upper body

Over the head

First method - sleeves off, then over the head

Position - sitting or lying.

Fabric - stretchy or half open back garment.

a. Gather garment up to first armhole, stronger arm first.

b. Slip sleeve down the arm, allowing the weight of the arm to slip out of the sleeve. Repeat for second sleeve. Ease collar over the head.

c. In this picture, the way in which the carer is holding the other arm and the way the garment is being taken off, is keeping the child in the correct position; once the garment is over the head, the carer must support the head.

For an older person, the back of a chair or a pillow will provide support. If the weight of the arm is not enough to pull the sleeve off, pull the armhole down as far as the elbow, ease over the elbow, and then pull off the rest of the sleeve.

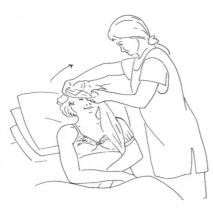

For someone able to hold the arms up beside the head, it may be possible to grasp the garment at the hem and pull it straight up and off. The garment will come off inside out.

Second method - first arm off, then head, then second arm

Positions - sitting and lying down.

Fabric - stretchy.

a. Bring garment up as far as both armholes.

b. Ease sleeve off from shoulder as far as elbow, then pull off rest of arm.

Move upper body forward to pull up rest of garment.

Gather garment on side of undressed arm and bring over the head.

Draw off other sleeve.

Front opening

First method

Position - sitting.

a. Unfasten. Pull garment up to the neck on one/weaker side.

b. Ease fabric down the other arm as far as the elbow, bend the elbow, push the fabric round and take off the arm.

Bend the body forward enough to bring garment round the back.

Draw off second sleeve.

Second method

Position - seated

a. Unfasten garment, stand behind chair. The person leans forward slightly, leaning on a table. Carer lifts garment on one side and puts hand into armhole.

b. Ease sleeve down arm as far as elbow, bring round elbow and ease off arm.

Repeat for other arm.

Third method

Position - lying.

a. Ease first sleeve off either by method previously described, or by holding sleeve by cuff, lifting arm in sleeve, and allowing weight of arm to slide out.

OR Roll onto one side, bring one arm back and bring sleeve down arm.

b. Roll person towards carer if arm furthest away has been undressed, away from carer if the nearest one has been undressed. Tuck garment into the back and return person to original position.

Take other sleeve off in the same way.

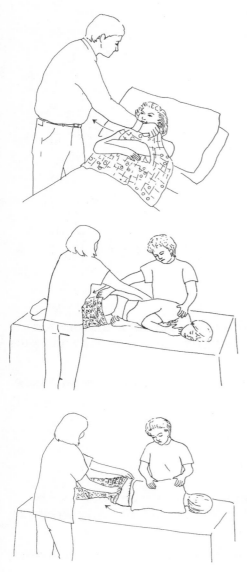

Back opening

Positions - sitting and lying down.

a. *(sitting)* Lean forward.

(lying) Roll towards carer.

Unfasten any fastenings.

b. Bring edges of garment to sides.

(sitting) Lean person back in chair.

(lying) Roll back in bed.

Draw off each sleeve in turn .

Garments for lower body

First method - rolling person by two people

Position - lying.

a. Roll person to one side with head well supported.

b. Pull garment down over hips on that side. Roll over to other side, pull garment down and over the feet.

Second method - pushing garment down legs

(An example of self-help where child must be kept in correct position.)

Position - lying (on floor).

a. Helper kneels down and encloses the child's feet between his/her knees. Hold onto child's hands. Undo any fastenings.

b. Pull child up and forward; roll garment off hips, one side at a time, holding on to one hand to keep him/her forward.

Using child's hand, help him/her to push the trouser legs down and then to pull off, keeping child forward all the time.

Wrap around

Position - lying.

a. Unfasten.

b. Take edges of garment to sides and tuck under one edge.

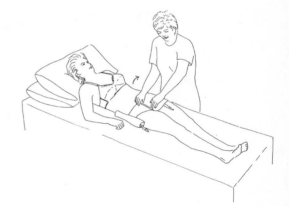

Roll person onto that side and remove garment.

Half-open-back dress, coat etc

Opening needs to be below the waist

Positions - sitting and lying.

a. Roll person to one side. Unfasten.

b. Ease off uppermost sleeve.

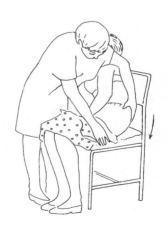

Roll onto other side; ease off other sleeve.

Ease garment down to hips.

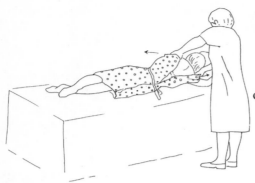

Roll to one side, ease over hip.

Roll back onto other side. Ease over other hip.

Draw garment off legs and over feet.

c. *(lying)* This method could be reversed, bringing garment over the hips and up over the head and off the arms.

This method can also be used for half-open front garment

Front opening

Position - sitting.

a. Undo fastenings.

b. Push garment off shoulders.

Hold first arm and ease out of sleeve.

Repeat with other arm.

Leave garment on chair.

Over the head

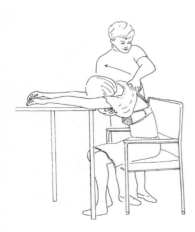

Position - sitting.

Fabric - stretchy or sleeveless garment.

a. Bring skirt over hips by rolling or standing.

b. Rest arms on support.

Bring garment up to armholes, lift garment over head from back.

Ease sleeves down arms.

Shoes, hosiery

Positions - sitting, lying.

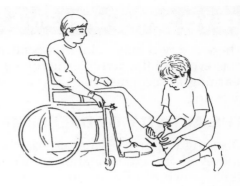

a. Undo fastenings (stockings, socks). Bring hosiery down legs as far as ankles.

b. Support heel with one hand, take garment off foot with the other. Repeat.

c. Note any areas of redness on feet or oedema.

DEVELOPING DRESSING SKILLS

There are two major skills associated with dressing. The first is mastering all the activities involved in dressing; the second is learning to recognise the various garments and their relationship to dressing.

THE ACTIVITY OF DRESSING

Dressing requires both motor development (control over muscles) and eye-hand co-ordination (when hands and eyes work together), skills which a child usually learns in an orderly, predictable fashion following a definite sequence.

A young child develops the following skills in order to learn how to dress.

- Motor development in the young child starts with the ability to control his head. Gradually, this ability extends to his arms, hands, trunk and legs, until he can balance on one leg and carry on an activity without falling over.

- As he develops eye-hand co-ordination, and learns to use his thumb and fingers, his vague uncoordinated movements will be transformed into controlled and finely executed ones.

The development of dressing and undressing skills follows the same pattern.

- Control of the head enables the child to push his head through the necks of vests and jumpers.

- Control of the arms enables him to hold out his arms for sleeves and push his arms through.

- Control of the hands enables him to pull socks and slippers off.

- Control of fingers enables him to do up buttons.

- Control of the legs enables him to step out of trousers and pants and hold out his feet for socks and shoes

Having learnt to control these simple activities he will then go on to master the following, more complex ones:

- Once he can stand up, he balances first by holding onto someone or something; once able to pull on his garments by himself, he may prefer to sit down to put on clothes for the lower body until he feels sure enough of his balance to stand on one leg.

- Once the eyes can co-ordinate with the fine movements of hands and fingers, the child will be able to recognise the various parts of the garments so that they can be put on correctly, and will be able to master all types of fastening.
- With greater experience, much of the eye-hand co-ordination involved in finding armholes, adjusting waistbands and doing up fastenings followed by back bows and neckties (with the help of a mirror) is gradually replaced by 'touch'.

Once dressing skills have been mastered they become virtually automatic, and few people will need to give the activity of dressing any conscious thought unless forced to do so because they have had an accident or developed a disability.

LEARNING TO RECOGNISE CLOTHES

This involves:

- recognising the different items of clothing;
- learning the order and the way in which clothes are put on.

Recognising clothes

There are numerous items of clothing, many serving the same purpose. They can be distinguished by:

1. shape;

2. the way they are put on and taken off;

3. by look and by name;

4. colour;

5. touch - especially important for people with a visual impairment.

The order and orientation of clothes

If clothes are put on, taken off and laid out in the same order every time, the order becomes part of a daily pattern.

Distinguishing between back and front

Distinguishing between the back and front of garments is easy in relation to front opening clothes and fly-front trousers, but not so easy in the case of over-the-head clothes and pull-up pants or trousers.

Useful hints:

- clothes can be marked so that the back can be distinguished from the front or use can be made of the manufacturer's tab;
- the feeling of discomfort experienced when some garments are worn the wrong way round may help;
- laying out clothes front downwards;
- bras may be a problem; they are best held up before attempting to put them on.

Left and right

The difference between right and left is important in relation to gloves and footwear. Fabric gloves can be worn on the wrong hands without too much discomfort; leather and rubber ones can not; slippers and wellington boots are easier to wear on the wrong feet than walking shoes.

Useful hints:

- marking clothes and looking at the garment and comparing it with the correct hand or foot may be helpful;
- buckles on footwear are usually on the outside of the foot.

Top and bottom

Relating clothing to the different parts of the body can help people to distinguish top from bottom.

Useful hints:

- since arms and head are at the top of the body, sleeves and neck must also be at the top;
- holding up clothes correctly, finding the largest hole, placing garments against oneself, and talking about top and bottom may be helpful.

Inside and outside

The difference between the inside and outside of garments may be difficult to distinguish when both sides look the same.

Useful hints:

- a lining, the position of fastenings, seams and makers' tabs provide good clues;

- a knitted fabric is smooth on the outside and rough on the inside;
- many T-shirts and sweaters have the maker's name or a picture on the outside;
- taking off the garment without turning it inside out may help.

TEACHING DRESSING SKILLS

The need to re-learn dressing skills will usually arise as the result of an accident or because someone has developed a chronic illness. Anyone can teach dressing skills, but whoever does so should work as part of a team, with the help of professionals - occupational therapists, physiotherapists and others.

People with brain damage may be spatially disoriented (ie not know where they are in space) or have perceptual motor dysfunction (ie know what ought to be done but cannot carry it out). Therefore, although they may appear to understand what to do, it is possible that they do not, or that they may be able to do it one day but not the next.

Dressing is a complex procedure and in these circumstances is best taught after someone, usually an occupational therapist, has helped the person to increase his/her concentration and attention span. An assessment can then be made of any gaps in the person's knowledge and teaching concentrated on these.

Hints for teaching

- Assess the personality, comprehension, abilities and willpower of the learner.
- Draw up a learning programme, progressing from simple to complex procedures. Each procedure should be mastered before going on to the next one.
- Demonstrate the procedure to the learner who should practise it regularly, if possible at the right time of day. Constant repetition may be necessary using the same words. Use of a mirror can be helpful.
- The pace of teaching should be matched to the ability of the learner.
- If help is required, decide when it should be given during the procedure, and change it according to progress.
- All accomplishments, however small, should be praised.

- The frustration of those re-learning dressing needs to be understood and ways sought to overcome it.
- The teacher should be enthusiastic and willing to try new methods and involve the learner in these.

ASSESSING THE ABILITY TO DRESS

The capabilities of elderly and disabled people, wherever they live, should be regularly assessed as part of the total care programme. Dressing should be part of that assessment. Would some dressing practice be helpful? Would different fastenings or clothes be easier?

Therapists and district nurses can be asked to help with this kind of advice. Although not all elderly people require special help or adaptations, many could benefit from information about easier clothing to wear or other ways of dressing and undressing.

The attitude of those caring for disabled or elderly people has a considerable effect upon those they support. If the carer deprives the person being cared for of any type of challenge, this can affect the atmosphere in which they live, and the morale of all. It may be easier for the helper to help someone to dress when it is not really necessary. That person may then feel that dressing does not matter and give up. A constant interest in how he looks and helping to gain maximum independence in dressing may have benefits in other parts of his life.

The first assessment of dressing abilities should, if possible, be undertaken by a therapist. However, if no therapist is available, an assessment can be made by:

a) asking the person to put and take off:

   i   a loose garment over the head

   ii   a stretchy open-front garment with short and long sleeves

   iii pants or knickers, trousers if appropriate

   iv slippers and shoes

   v   hosiery

   vi foundation garments, as appropriate

   vii a necktie;

b) testing his/her ability to cope with different fastenings:

   i   zips, in front and behind

   ii   buttons - shirt and coat size, and different shapes

   iii press studs of all sizes

   iv laces, including shoes

v   buckles

vi   velcro.

During the initial assessment, help should not be given unless it is absolutely necessary. The procedure should be explained first. During the assessment the carer should note which openings and fastenings can be managed most easily, which movements are easiest and/or least painful, and the amount of energy required. This information can then be used to decide on the most suitable garments, fastenings, dressing aids, adaptations and dressing methods, and, if necessary, a programme of training planned for particular difficulties and special techniques.

The degree to which someone can use his/her hands usually dictates how much dressing is possible. Significant overweight compounds any disability by increasing the workload of muscles and joints. Always remember that the energy used in dressing and undressing must be balanced against the energy required for other activities.

Everyone should be assessed regularly, preferably by the same person, to see what progress has been made. It can be done as part of a normal dressing session.

CONDITIONS FOR DRESSING

Dressing should take place in the best possible environment.

1. Time

Make sure that enough time is set aside to dress.

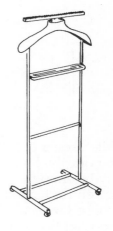

Someone who is rushed may be confused, give up too easily or need help. Equally, someone who is left too long may forget what he is doing, or even take off garments. Time also encourages experiment.

It saves time if garments are laid out in order and at the right level. Putting them out the evening before, on a chair or valet stand, helps. Shoes should be placed where they can be reached easily.

2. Privacy and warmth

These are essential for all personal activities.

3. Space

Make sure that there is enough space for both the carer and the dresser to manoeuvre.

4. Assistance

Help can be given at any time or limited to seeing that everything is ready for dressing to start. How much assistance is given will depend upon the needs and personality of the individual being helped. It may be better to give help at the start and leave the person who is dressing to finish, or more challenging to leave the him/her to start and offer help at the end. For those who are striving for independence, assistance should only be given when absolutely necessary.

5. Suitable furnishings

The floor should have a non-slip surface. If a chair is used for dressing, it should be high enough for both feet to be placed flat on the floor, be stable, and have arms if support is needed.

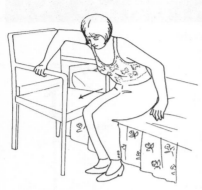

If a bed is used, it should have a firm covering, ie no coverlet or quilt, with a firm level edge; have enough pillows; be able to support various aids, eg a loop ladder or pulley if required; be high enough so that the person dressing can put both feet flat on the floor when sitting on the side; be the same height as the chair if the dresser transfers from one to the other.

Stable furniture, such as a heavy chest of drawers, can be used as a support while dressing. If the dresser needs to lean on something temporarily, light furniture place against a wall or the wall itself may be enough. A solid chair placed beside the bed may provide enough protection if someone has a tendency to fall to one side. A stool or low chair can be helpful when putting on hosiery and shoes. Good lighting is important.

A mirror is essential for almost everyone. We all use one when straightening a jacket, positioning a tie or to make sure that everything matches. It is useful for dressing practice, maintaining body image and assessing how we look.

A mirror should be at the right height and placed in a good light. (If someone is inclined to be confused by his/her mirror image, then a mirror should not be used.)

7. Equipment for walking or dressing

Such equipment should always be near to hand and be well supported so that an accidental movement cannot knock it out of reach.

8. Willingness to experiment

Experimentation helps both the dresser and the carer to keep an open mind. For instance.

- if putting on nightwear is too exhausting at the end of the day, it might be easier to sleep in the nude;

- men's shoes are made on a wider last, so some women may find that such shoes fit them better;

- it is not always easy to persuade an elderly woman to give up wearing her corsets, although the struggle to put them on may become too much for her. She can keep up her stockings in a number of other ways, or she may be persuaded to change the fastenings.

9. Position

Each individual will find the best position in which to dress him/herself - standing, sitting or on the bed, and all other possible combinations. When someone is being helped to dress, the helper will probably have some influence on this.

PLACE OF DRESSING IN REHABILITATION

Rehabilitation starts almost as soon as someone becomes disabled, whatever the cause. Its aim is to reduce the disability to a minimum and to help the person with the disability to regain basic personal skills. Even where this seems unlikely, the aim should be kept firmly in mind.

Since dressing involves using most of the muscles of the body, balance, manipulative ability, knowledge of colour and eye-hand co-ordination, it can be used therapeutically.

It helps to mobilise joints and muscles, provides a definite, practical aim and discloses which movements still need to be taught. It is an essential activity of daily living, upon which going home from hospital may depend. Rehabilitation is often a long-term process so it is important to teach the carer how to continue the routine at home.

Any training programme should start with undressing as it takes less energy than dressing. When re-learning to dress, tackle the easiest garments first to avoid frustration and fatigue.

Brain damage will affect progress in rehabilitation, and this is particularly noticeable following a stroke or similar event. Mental illness may affect comprehension and motivation. It is important that the motive for encouraging independence is right - to enable the person to achieve/enhance personal satisfaction and /or to return to normal social/work activities.

WHERE TO GET HELP

Since it is impossible for one profession or one person to be the repository of all skills and knowledge, teamwork is essential.

Dressing and undressing

Professional advice on dressing and undressing should be available from:

- occupational therapists, who are experts in the field of daily living activities and can help to evaluate different techniques, clothes, adaptations and aids;

- physiotherapists, who are experts in the field of movement, and can suggest techniques of dressing which use specific muscles and joints, using a dressing technique as physiotherapy;

- speech and language therapists, who may be able to help people who dribble;
- stoma therapists, who can advise on suitable clothing and how to minimise or eliminate leaks;
- continence advisers, who can advise on suitable protection.

These professionals are available for consultation and advice both in a person's own home as well as in hospital departments. However, since they can only spend a limited amount of time with each person while the helper is there for 24 hours, it is important that the treatment or programme started by such staff is explained to helpers so that they can continue it. This sort of teamwork, which includes both the patient and the helper, is more likely to produce positive results.

Clothing

1. For people in their own homes, advice is available from:

- a number of books and leaflets (see inside back cover);
- other helpers/carers and people with similar difficulties (see useful addresses, Appendix 5).

2. In residential accommodation:

Each home will have its own policy for residents' clothes. If clothes are washed on the premises, they may have to have name-tapes and some fabrics may not be accepted.

3. In hospital and long term care:

Clothing may be provided and professional advice on clothes should be available from:

- supplies officers;
- laundry managers;
- sewing room supervisors and tailors;
- clothing managers who should co-ordinate policy.

Although clothing is usually provided, all establishments should now operate a policy that enable residents to have their own clothing, which they can choose for themselves, have washed nearby, and be stored within reach. See the DLF's *Clothing: a quality issue*.

USEFUL ADDRESSES

Age Concern England
Astral House
1268 London Road
London SW16 4EJ
081 679 8000

Alzheimer's Disease Society
Gordon House
10 Greencoat Place
London SW1P 1PH
071 306 0606

Arthritis Care
18 Stephenson Way
London NW1 2HD
071 916 1500 / 1505

**Association for Spina Bifida
and Hydrocephalus (ASBAH)**
ASBAH House
42 Park Road
Peterborough PE1 2UQ
0733 555988

Brittle Bone Society
c/o Mrs M Grant
112 City Road
Dundee DD2 2PW
0382 817771

**Carer's National
Association**
20-25 Glasshouse Yard
London
EC1A 4JS
071 490 8898

Continence Foundation
Basement
2 Doughty Street
London WC1N 2PH
071 404 6875

Disability Scotland
Princes House
5 Shandwick Place
Edinburgh EH2 4RG
031 229 8632

**Down's Syndrome
Association**
155 Mitcham Road
London SW17 9PG
081 682 4001

Help the Aged
16-18 St James Walk
London EC1R 0BE
071 253 0253

Limbless Association
31 The Mall
Ealing
London W5 2PX
081 579 1758

MENCAP
117 - 123 Golden Lane
London EC1Y 0RT
071 454 0454

Multiple Sclerosis Society of Great Britain
25 Effie Road
London SW6 1EE
071 371 8000

Muscular Dystrophy Group
7-11 Prescott Place
London SW4 6BS
071 720 8055

National Back Pain Association
The Old Office Block
Elmtree Road
Teddington
Middlesex TW11 8ST
081 977 5474

National Eczema Society
4 Tavistock Place
London WC1H 9RA
071 388 4097

National Osteoporosis Society
PO Box 10
Radstock
Bath BA3 3YB

Parkinson's Disease Society
22 Upper Woburn Place
London WC1N 0RA
071 383 3513

Restricted Growth Association
c/o Mrs T Webb
103 St Thomas' Avenue
West Town
Hayling Island
Hants, PO11 0EU
0705 461813

Royal Association for Disability and Rehabilitation (RADAR)
12 City Forum
250 City Road
London EC1V 8AF
071 250 3222

Royal National Institute for the Blind (RNIB)

224-228 Great Portland Street

London W1N 6AA

071 388 1266

SCOPE (formally Spastic Society)

12 Park Crescent

London W1N 4EQ

071 636 5020

Scoliosis Association UK

2 Ivebury Court

323 Latimer Road

London W10 6RA

Spinal Injuries Association

76 St James' Lane

London N10 3DF

081 444 2121

Stroke Association

CHSA House

Whitecross Street

London EC17 8JJ

071 490 7999

INDX

INDEX

A

Absorption/water repellence	3
Adapting fastenings	35
Adapting garments	35
Asthma	53

B

Back opening garments	63, 81, 92, 94, 100
Back pain	52
Blouses	37
Boot remover	32
Boxer shorts	22
Braces	15
Bras	20, 35, 36
Bridging	58
Briefs	22
'Broomstick' plasters	50
Buckles	11
Burns	51
Buttonhook	29
Buttonholes and loops	9
Buttons	35
Buttons - magnetic	9
Buttons and toggles	8

C

Cami-knickers	21
Caring for your clothes	5
Choosing clothes for easy dressing	1
'Coat-on'	32
Coats	38
Conceptual difficulties	33
Continence equipment	48
Continence Foundation	48
Corsets	21, 35, 36

H

I

J

K

L

M